Follow us on social media!

Tag us and use #piccadillyinc in your posts
for a chance to win monthly prizes!

This edition published by Piccadilly (USA) Inc.

Piccadilly (USA) Inc.
12702 Via Cortina, Suite 203
Del Mar, CA 92014
USA

10 9 8 7 6 5 4 3 2 1

Printed in China

ISBN-13: 978-1-62009-688-8

1 What is your idea of perfect happiness?

2 What is your greatest fear?

3 What is the trait you most deplore in yourself?

4 What is your greatest extravagance?

5 What is your current state of mind?

6 What do you consider the most overrated virtue?

7 On what occasion do you lie?

8 What do you most dislike about your appearance?

9 Which living person do you most despise?

10 What is the quality you most like in a man?

11 What is the quality you most like in a woman?

12 Which words or phrases do you most overuse?

13 What or who is the greatest love of your life?

14 When and where were you happiest?

15 Which talent would you most like to have?

16 If you could change one thing about yourself, what would it be?

17 What do you consider your greatest achievement?

18 If you were to die and come back as a person or a thing, what would it be?

19 Where would you most like to live?

20 What is your most treasured possession?

21 What do you regard as the lowest depth of misery?

22 What is your favorite occupation?

23 What is your most marked characteristic?

24 What do you most value in your friends?

25 Who are your favorite writers?

26 Who is your hero of fiction?

27 Which historical figure do you most identify with?

28 Who are your heroes in real life?

29 What are your favorite names?

30 What is it that you most dislike?

31 What is your greatest regret?

32 How would you like to die?

33 What is your motto?

34 Do you like watching reruns?

35 Have you ever won any kind of contest yourself?

36 What gives you cheap thrills?

37 What do you think is worth waiting for?

38 Are you an organ donor, if so why/why not?

39 Should parenting classes be mandatory for new parents?

40 What is the number one thing people are always asking you for help with?

41 What movie did you love the original but hate the sequel?

42 Are you more talk and less action or vice versa?

43 Have you ever given someone a handmade present?

44 What type of person angers you the most?

45 Could you live without electricity for a week?

46 Do you think Great Britain should be part of a united Europe?

47 Have you ever eaten a whole tube of Pringles by yourself?

48 Do you like champagne, if so what is your favorite brand?

49 What nervous habits do you have?

50 What do you do when you and your best friend get into a fight?

51 What do you think should be a wonder of the world that currently isn't?

52 What comforts you on bad days?

53 Do you treat yourself and your body with respect?

54 Something you eat that other people would find gross.

55 Have you ever broken the law and didn't get caught, if so how?

56 Something you fear might change you.

57 What personality trait in people raises a red flag with you?

58 Have you ever resented someone, if so what for?

59 Do you have a favorite t-shirt, if so what's on it or what does it say?

60 How old do you think is too old to have a baby?

61 How have you changed over the last 5 years?

62 Have you ever painted a house?

63 Have you ever had a surprise party (that was an actual surprise)?

64 What makes you feel miserable?

65 What's the best costume you've ever worn?

66 What's been the hardest loss you've had to take?

67 Do you like sunny days or rainy days more?

68 What does your typical Friday night look like?

69 Who is your favorite movie director and what's your favorite movie from them?

70 What is the furthest you've ever got a paper airplane to fly?

71 Do you like the person you're becoming?

72 What's the highest you've ever jumped into the water from?

73 What inspires your ideas?

74 Have you ever assembled furniture by yourself?

75 Have you ever bolstered your resume to get a job you really wanted?

76 How emotional are you?

77 Have you ever had an internship, if not what would be your dream intern job?

78 Do you prefer chicken, beef or seafood?

79 Have you ever had a health scare?

80 What do you love most about the holiday season?

81 Do you think a fling could be a good thing?

82 What part of your routine do you always try to skip if you can?

83 What do or did you hate most about dating or the dating process?

84 What do you frown upon when it comes to raising kids?

85 Have you ever been professionally photographed?

86 Where or how do you find serenity?

87 Do you influence people more than they influence you?

88 What can you do to make your life better?

89 If you could ask one person, alive or dead, only one question, what would you ask?

90 What is your favorite hiding place?

91   Do you buy anything organic, if so what?

92   Describe yourself in terms of food.

93   How could you reinvent yourself?

94   What was the name of the first album you ever bought and who was it by?

95   What is your Chinese zodiac sign and is the description accurate?

96   Do you have any prejudices you've admitted to yourself?

97   Who is the very first friend you ever remember making and how old were you?

98   What makes you lose sleep?

99   What are 3 phrases or sayings you say almost every day?

100   Do you floss or use a toothpick when food gets stuck in your teeth?

101   Have you ever swerved off the road to avoid hitting something?

102   Compare your driving skills to something?

103   What food is romantic to you?

104   Do you forgive and forget, just forgive but not forget or neither?

105   Have you ever had an out of body experience? If so describe it in one word.

106　How easy is it for you to get along with people?

107　Has someone ever given you a "last chance" and for what?

108　Something on your "to-do list" that never gets done.

109　What's your favorite thing to eat with your fingers?

110　What is your favorite or most used cookbook?

111　What food best describes your personality?

112　Would you ever do a ride along with a cop, if so what do you want to see?

113　Do you think ignorance is bliss?

114　Are you a pacifist?

115　What do you need to do to grow?

116　What is something you wish you learned?

117　Where's your favorite place to order pizza?

118　Who taught you how to drive?

119　If you were to ever win a Nobel Peace Prize, what do you think it would be for?

120　Do you ask enough questions or do you settle for what you know?

121 Have you ever helped someone across the road?

122 What is legal that you think should be illegal?

123 Would you rather own a private jet or luxury yacht?

124 What's the first impression you want to give people?

125 Which would you rather have if you had to, a broken leg or a broken arm?

126 What profession do you think is the most undervalued today?

127 What is your favorite thing to put icecream on or eat icecream with?

128 Who would you love to collaborate with and what would you collaborate on?

129 Where do you cut costs when you need to save?

130 What was one thing you begged your parents for as a kid and they finally gave it to you?

131 If you could have someone serenade you over a candle light dinner, who would it be?

132 Do you think horoscopes are accurate?

133 How do you describe millennials?

134 What have you ever ran from that you needed to face?

135 What makes you unique?

136 Do you have a pet, if so what kind?

137 If you were a bartender what famous person would you like to serve?

138 If you could choose your last words, what would they be?

139 Do you have a calling on your life?

140 Have you ever let someone win an argument even if you knew you were right, if so who?

141 Could you ever be a medical guinea pig?

142 What is the most annoying thing about the opposite sex?

143 How do you feel about investing your money?

144 What is something you'd like to grow instead of buying?

145 How do you like to take your coffee or tea?

146 How smart is your significant other, who is smarter?

147 What is your preferred swimming stroke?

148 Have you ever had something snowball out of control, if so what?

149 What is the likelihood you'll make the half-court at a game for some serious cash?

150 What is the main thing you like to do on vacations?

151 Were you popular in school, if so what made you popular?

152 What risk would you take if you knew you wouldn't fail?

153 What was an offer you couldn't refuse?

154 Do you believe in angels?

155 If you were guaranteed the correct answer to one question, what would you ask?

156 Would you rather lose all of your old memories or never be able to make new ones?

157 Have you ever been at the wrong place at the wrong time, where?

158 Have you ever been whistled at in public?

159 What is something totally relatable to you?

160 What's the best pickup line you've ever heard?

161 Would you ever steal to provide for your family?

162 In your opinion who do you consider a visionary?

163 If you could live forever, would you want to?

164 What or who are you a champion for?

165 What is your favorite store at the mall?

166   Have you ever touched a snake or would you?

167   What do you think gets better with age?

168   Do you ever forward or reply to chain mails?

169   What scientist in history is most credible?

170   Have you ever been called immature, if so what were you doing to be called that?

171   Is there a place in your neighborhood or city you've been meaning to visit, if so where?

172   What slogan or jingle got stuck in your head forever?

173   Could you ever grow your own food?

174   If you could be a bird, which would you be?

175   Do you watch foreign films, if so do you have a favorite?

176   What specific work of art do you admire the most?

177   Which are cooler: dinosaurs or dragons?

178   Has your work ever come between a relationship you were in, if so how?

179   Have you ever needed to find yourself and if so are you still looking?

180   What is your all-time favorite selfie, and what was going on in it?

181   If you could have a clone to help you out when life gets busy, would you want one?

182   What are you "self-taught"?

183   The Beatles or Rolling Stones?

184   What do you try and keep an open mind about?

185   Would you rather ride along with a firefighter or police officer for a day?

186   Do you believe in the saying kill your enemies with kindness?

187   What do you love most about the night sky?

188   In an argument do you have to have the last word?

189   Have you ever participated in a fundraiser, if so for what cause?

190   What is the heaviest thing you can lift?

191   Would you ever consider training for a triathlon?

192   What is your perfect pairing for coffee?

193   How strict are you going to be as a parent?

194   Who do you matter most to?

195   What movie director do you find completely genius?

196 What's your favorite hobby?

197 Do you think a person can be born evil?

198 Do you believe in PDA (public displays of affection)?

199 Would you date anyone in a wheelchair or with a handicap?

200 What is an article of clothing you've bought or received second hand and loved wearing?

201 Who would you rather hang out with for a day–Superman or Batman?

202 What makes you feel secure?

203 Do you sing in the shower?

204 What makes you feel inadequate?

205 What does your perfect weekend consist of?

206 If you could live anywhere, where would that be?

207 Do you have a nerdy side, if so what brings it out?

208 Do you think children are a blessing or a burden?

209 What's the hardest thing you've ever had to plan?

210 What is the best knock-knock joke you've heard?

211 What is your greatest source of inspiration?

212 What's the wildest thing you've ever done?

213 If you could be trained in any one thing by top professionals what would you choose?

214 What is the highest hill or mountain you've ever climbed?

215 Do you think making driverless cars is a smart invention?

216 Use a cartoon character to describe your athletic ability.

217 Do you like to plan things out in detail or be spontaneous?

218 Do you like living alone or with someone?

219 Do you make time for what matters most for you?

220 What makes you feel unattractive?

221 How many hats do you own?

222 Have you ever contributed to the development of something you were proud of?

223 What is your favorite song to sing in the shower?

224 Do you make a "to-do list" every day, weekly or when?

225 If a loved one was to serenade you, what song would you most like them to sing?

226 What is your opinion on rats as pets?

227 Were you ever really passionate about something then suddenly lost interest, what was it?

228 Which was your favorite science? Biology, physics or chemistry?

229 Can you erect a tent?

230 Have you ever received counseling or therapy and did it help?

231 Have you ever sued or wanted to sue someone, why?

232 Who would you want to star opposite you, if you were in a movie?

233 Do you believe in the death penalty?

234 Have you ever done something to your parents that you regretted?

235 Have you ever nicknamed someone and it stuck, if so who and what was the nickname?

236 If you knew you would die tomorrow, would you feel cheated today?

237 Who influenced your life the most?

238 What is the simplest truth you can express in words?

239 Have you ever been famous?

240 Have you ever posted a video on YouTube, what was the video about?

241 Do you prefer music on vinyl or streaming?

242 What do you do when you get nervous?

243 Where's your favorite place to get coffee or tea?

244 Did you ever have an embarrassing moment in gym class in school?

245 What do you love most about yourself?

246 If you started a business tomorrow what would it be?

247 What is one thing you've learned about people over the years?

248 How judgmental are you towards other people?

249 What's your ratio of naughty to nice?

250 What is history's most tragic love story in your opinion?

251 Have you ever went after anything (job, relationship, etc.) and didn't get it?

252 Which activities make you lose track of time?

253 In what way has money impacted you negatively?

254 What celebrity designer would you want to redo your home?

255 Do you believe in an eye for an eye?

256   How was your very first kiss?

257   What age would you not want to live past?

258   What celebrity do you think got carried away with plastic surgery?

259   If you could hire any wedding singer, who would you choose and what song?

260   What age do you think is too young to get married?

261   What one thing do you think all successful leaders have in common?

262   Have you ever donated blood and if so do you do it regularly?

263   Do you have a birthmark, if so where?

264   Do you prefer watching a movie at home or at a theater?

265   Are you much of a gambler?

266   Do you believe confession is good for the soul?

267   If you could own one famous original work of art, what piece would it be?

268   Do you sometimes spend money you don't have or live above your means?

269   Do you have a specific disease that runs in your family that worries you?

270   As a kid were you ever frightened of a monster under the bed and what did it look like?

271 Would you break the law to save a loved one?

272 Do you like to receive bad news sugarcoated or bluntly?

273 Do you think celebrities should be looked at as a role model or just for entertainment?

274 Do you believe in God or a higher power?

275 Where is your favorite place to meditate?

276 If you ever decided to run for President, what would be your campaign slogan?

277 After a long, hard day at work or school, what do you like to do?

278 If you could bankrupt one person or company who would it be?

279 Who texts you the most, and why?

280 What's the best excuse you've given or would give to a bill collector?

281 If you were going on *Dancing with the Stars*, whom would you want as your partner?

282 Have you ever made your own icecream?

283 Do you prefer your hair longer or shorter?

284 What public figure do you disagree with the most?

285 Do you buy people mementos when you go on vacation?

286 Describe Mondays for you in one word.

287 Have you ever ran out of gas in your car, if so where?

288 What does honor mean to you in a few words?

289 Have you ever been on a group outing, where did you go?

290 Do you like throwing parties?

291 Have you ever been on TV?

292 What is your idea of moral support?

293 Do you own a camera and if so what was the last photo you took?

294 If you could challenge anyone to a boxing match, whom would you want to fight?

295 What do you think still has a double standard?

296 Did you ever skip school before and if so what did you do instead?

297 Do you prefer water skiing or snow skiing?

298 Rate your table etiquette on a scale of 1-10 with 10 being outstanding and 1 being awful.

299 What song makes you dance uncontrollably?

300 Have you ever tried a savory pie, if so what kind?

301 What is the most dangerous thing you have ever done?

302 Have you ever dated someone your parents didn't like?

303 Which do you prefer: pony tails or pig tails?

304 When have you ever made the first move?

305 Have you ever felt violated and if so in what way?

306 What are you superstitious about?

307 Where are you considered a regular at?

308 If you were a super hero what would your hero name be?

309 In the haste of your daily life, what are you not remembering?

310 What is the best thing about being you?

311 What is the most important thing to carry with you all the time?

312 When you find someone physically attractive, what's the first thing you notice?

313 What is the most cliché thing you have done in your life?

314 What do you feel is the perfect food for a food fight?

315 What is your most favorite feature on your favorite electronic device?

316 A wish you make again and again.

317 Have you ever been on a blind date?

318 Are you OCD about anything?

319 What happened to put you at your lowest low?

320 How do you get into the holiday spirit?

321 When people look you in the eyes, what do you hope they see?

322 For your wedding ceremony do you want it big and elaborate or small and intimate?

323 What is your favorite sci-fi film/program etc.?

324 Have you ever played a practical joke on anyone?

325 Do you have a crush right now? Who is it?

326 Have you ever helped someone through a trauma?

327 When you were a kid did you ever want to run away from home, if so why?

328 Do you have any lucky items, objects or traditions?

329 What is the tallest tree you've ever climbed?

330 Describe your sense of humor in one word.

331 What has required you to put constant thought into it?

332 Do you have any questions you're just too scared or embarrassed to ask anyone about?

333 What is your favorite actress beginning with the letter J?

334 What was the hardest personal goal you've set for yourself?

335 Do you operate with the motto "it's my way or the highway" and if so does it work for you?

336 What's the last thing you've done that you were really proud of?

337 Would you win more money at *Jeopardy* or *Wheel of Fortune?*

338 What are you really lazy about?

339 Have you ever used the phrase "back in my time" to someone younger than you?

340 Which is better, Mario or Sonic?

341 What do you think one of the biggest cons about being famous would be?

342 Has anyone or anything specific ever made you feel inferior, if so what?

343 Do you think stay at home mothers should be paid a salary?

344 What would the scariest place to get lost at?

345 Besides a pickle, what is your favorite thing that's pickled?

346 Do you sing to yourself?

347 How many of your friends would you trust with your life?

348 Do you have an image of something you'll never forget?

349 Have you ever demolished a wall or building?

350 What nickname have you been called you hate?

351 What great mystery do you want solved?

352 What is your favorite movie that won an Oscar?

353 Have you ever felt like you didn't fit in, if so where or when was it?

354 Do you throw bread for the ducks?

355 What brings a tear of joy to your eye?

356 Do you think keeping animals in captivity is wrong?

357 What are you unapologetic for?

358 Do you like your music loud or quiet for easy listening?

359 How easy are you to satisfy?

360 Do you think home schooling is beneficial or harmful?

361 Has anything ever came to you in a vision or a dream?

362 If you were going to write a poem for the world, what would be the title and topic?

363 Have you ever done something heroic?

364 Have you ever maxed out your credit cards, on what?

365 What was the most obvious publicity stunt a celebrity ever pulled?

366 Do you like to describe what you see in the clouds?

367 What actor or actress do you think is too overrated?

368 What clothing designer do you LOVE?

369 Do your dreams ever tell you to do anything?

370 If you were going to poison someone, how would you do it?

371 What would you do in a world war situation?

372 Do you operate better at night or during the day?

373 Would you ever become a CIA agent, if so why?

374 If you were an attorney is there any type of criminal case you wouldn't defend?

375 What part of life would you put a BIG warning label on?

376   What relationship or friendship do you regret ended?

377   Have you ever bought someone jewelry?

378   What was the worst hairstyle you ever had?

379   Who knows you better than anyone else?

380   Have you ever licked a battery?

381   What black and white movie is your favorite?

382   Do you play any games on your smartphone, if so what's your favorite?

383   Do you have any family heirlooms?

384   If you had to lose one of your 5 senses, which one would you give up?

385   Have you ever gone through a transformation, if so what did it involve?

386   Are you a role model for anyone in your life?

387   What book have you read multiple times?

388   Is there ever a good time to be confrontational?

389   In a typical week how much time do you spend on the internet?

390   Are you happy with your life at this moment?

391 What is your smartphone missing that you wish the designer would add?

392 Have you ever worn clothing with the labels/tags still attached?

393 What would you do if you came face to face with a huntsman spider?

394 What song is your favorite to slow dance to?

395 What character flaw of yours is both good and bad?

396 What is something you just have not been able to get over, even as time passes?

397 Have you ever gotten into trouble and couldn't get yourself out? Who did you ask for help?

398 Have you ever drawn on a sleeping person?

399 What do you want written on your tombstone?

400 What's your favorite accent?

401 Have you ever done anything that was forbidden?

402 Would you risk being late to work and fired in order to save an injured dog?

403 Have you ever seen a tornado up close?

404 What movie do you wish had a sequel?

405 Do you like nachos, if so what topping is a MUST have?

406   What do you not take seriously enough?

407   Has anyone ever approached you thinking you were someone else?

408   How tech savvy are you?

409   Have you ever dated two people at the same time?

410   Name 3 things about where you live that you find most beautiful?

411   If you were to remain single for the rest of your life do you think you could be happy?

412   What is the worst thing that could happen to you on a date?

413   Do you sleep with the TV or radio on?

414   What is your favorite thing to celebrate?

415   What are you candid about?

416   What lies do you often tell yourself?

417   Have you ever snuck in somewhere you shouldn't have been, if so where?

418   What dish or food usually served hot, and do you think is better cold?

419   Do you tend to live in the past, present or future?

420   If you could ask your future self one question what would it be?

421 What's the worst thing your parents ever said to you?

422 What was your worst nightmare?

423 Do you hold a grudge?

424 Have you ever crashed a wedding?

425 In your opinion what is the most toxic personality trait?

426 How are you quirky?

427 Is there something missing from your life?

428 Too much is never enough of...?

429 Which is better, violins or pianos?

430 Do you have a secret place you go to when you want to be alone?

431 What's the funniest thing you've ever done to your parents?

432 Did you or will you go to prom?

433 What's your favorite season?

434 What is the most romantic poem you've ever heard, who wrote it?

435 Have you ever created an opportunity for anyone else?

436 Do you like energy drinks, if so what one is your favorite?

437 Could you fire someone you're friends with if it was your job?

438 How many people have you dated?

439 Who do you trust the most in your life?

440 Have you had a strange encounter that you can't explain or are scared to share?

441 What questions would you ask the older residents if you were visiting a nursing home?

442 Have you ever used the opposite sex restroom in an emergency, if not would you?

443 Do you read the labels on the food you buy or do you just buy what you like?

444 What is the craziest thing you've ever asked Siri?

445 In what way do you pamper yourself?

446 Do you like rap music, if so who is your favorite rapper?

447 If you were a psychologist, whom would you love to get on your couch for conversations?

448 Would you prefer either a chauffeur or private chef for one month as a gift?

449 Do you believe in psychics and their abilities?

450 What charity holds a special place in your heart?

451 Best message you ever got in a fortune cookie.

452 What is the worst smell you have ever smelled?

453 What was the most memorable class you've ever taken in school or college?

454 Where is the scariest place you've ever been stuck or trapped?

455 In your opinion is anything lacking from music today?

456 What would you do if you made a mistake and somebody died?

457 Have you ever had an adventure in babysitting?

458 How shy are you when you meet new people?

459 Have you ever had a blessing in disguise, what was it?

460 How fast can you say the alphabet?

461 What was your favorite movie that was based on a book first?

462 What is your favorite thing to challenge people to?

463 Have you ever been or would you ever allow yourself to be hypnotized?

464 What is something in your life you will never apologize for?

465 What do you think is totally inappropriate but is commonly seen in today's society?

466 Where is your favorite place to take a nap?

467 Do you have a scar, if so how did you get it?

468 How have you matured through the years?

469 Would you rather take a very long train ride or very long plane ride?

470 Do you have an area of your life that you are never satisfied with?

471 What do you think should be more regulated that is currently not?

472 How independent are you?

473 How much affection do you need to feel happy?

474 How would you do as a contestant on the reality game show *Survivor?*

475 What is your favorite author beginning with the letter R?

476 Who do you think you should stop spending time with?

477 Would you ever become a missionary?

478 Do you believe "it's a dog eat dog world" or do you have a different opinion?

479 Do you buy from thrift stores?

480 What do you think about romance?

481 What do you think about the vagabond lifestyle?

482 What 3 things would you leave in a time capsule for people to open in 50 years?

483 Would you raise your kids the way your parents raised you?

484 Does time heal all wounds or is that just a saying?

485 Do you ever watch movies with subtitles?

486 If you were in a band, what instrument/role would you play?

487 What is something you're doing you never thought you would do?

488 Working _____ hours a week is too much for me.

489 What is the weirdest food combination craving you've ever had?

490 Have you ever had to make a big decision without enough information, if so what did you do?

491 If you were having lunch with the Queen of England, what would you talk to her about?

492 What reoccurring lie did you always tell your parents or teachers?

493 Do you still watch cartoons, if so which one/s?

494 What is the worst thing about being your gender?

495 Have you ever made a homemade gift for someone, if so what?

496 Can you use chopsticks when you eat or have you tried?

497 What movie had the best special effects?

498 Have you ever been suspended from work or school, if so for what?

499 Have you ever cried at a movie?

500 Were you ever a girl scout/boy scout and if so what was the best thing you learned?

501 What do you wish had a delivery service that currently doesn't where you live?

502 What's the funniest Twitter handle you've ever heard?

503 What is your favorite clothing store?

504 Do you talk to yourself?

505 What grooming habit is essential to your daily life?

506 Out of your 5 senses, which is your strongest?

507 Would you ever launch an idea on Kickstarter?

508 Is your life more like the show *Friends* or *Married with Children*?

509 Do you actively show compassion for others, and if so how?

510 What do you try to avoid at all costs?

511   What is something you don't mind paying more money for?

512   Have you ever carried a torch for someone?

513   What has been your greatest sacrifice?

514   What do you think is more likely; Dracula or a werewolf?

515   If you had to teach something, what would you teach?

516   What's the funniest question you ever asked your parents when you were younger?

517   How good of a tipper are you when going out?

518   If you were going undercover for the CIA, what would you want your new cover story to be?

519   Have you ever eaten anything prepared by a celebrity chef?

520   How modern are you?

521   Are you a "fanatic" of anything or anyone?

522   What discovery have you recently made you feel is cutting edge?

523   Do you think cheerleaders are motivating or distracting at football games?

524   What was your favorite documentary or biography?

525   What is your favorite children's story?

526 What was the last thing you dressed in costume as?

527 What is the funniest pet name you've ever heard?

528 Are you much of a thrill seeker?

529 Do you wake up with a smile?

530 What is your favorite piece of jewelry?

531 Have you ever entered a talent contest? What was your act?

532 Have you ever faked your way through something, what?

533 How long do you think you'll live?

534 If your significant other went to jail, would you wait for them to get out?

535 Have you ever turned into a detective checking up on someone or something?

536 If you could ever take a street sign or sign from anywhere, what sign do you want?

537 What's the longest you've gone without speaking to your best friend, why?

538 If you were famous would you want a statue or a building named after you?

539 Have you ever saved anyone's life or has anyone ever saved yours?

540 Are the majority of your friends same sex or opposite sex?

541 How do you make the most of a bad situation?

542 What do you call your evening meal? Dinner or supper?

543 Is there such a thing as a bad challenge in your opinion?

544 Who do you always have to justify your actions to?

545 What is the quickest way to your heart?

546 Who's someone you'd like to trade places with for a day?

547 How open-minded are you?

548 Are you any good at burlap sack races?

549 What's the meanest thing you've said to someone?

550 Which would be impossible for you to give up for the rest of your life: soda or coffee?

551 How ambitious are you?

552 Do you think opposites attract?

553 What's the best thing about your life?

554 What color looks best on you?

555 Have you ever walked out on dinner with someone?

556   Have you ever needed an eye test?

557   Do you carry anything with you for self-defense when you leave your home?

558   If you could read minds, whose would you read first?

559   What weird behavior or habit did you have as a child that you ditched as you got older?

560   What do you consider both a blessing and a curse?

561   How do you get into your creative zone and do you have a creative ritual?

562   If you were entering a baking contest, what recipe would you make?

563   If you were out at dinner with no cash what would you do or say to get the bill paid?

564   What is an enemy to our existence or way of life?

565   Do you think Barbie is a negative role model for young girls?

566   If you saw a unicorn in the middle if the woods, what would you do?

567   When you have to study for a test, what is a proven successful method?

568   What's a common topic at your dinner table?

569   Have you ever thought about dating a really good friend?

570   Is change easy for you?

571 Who is your favorite dancer?

572 Did you do anything special for your 16th birthday, what?

573 If you wrote your will right now who would be the beneficiary?

574 What talent were you gifted, that comes natural?

575 Have you ever been disappointed by something you anticipated to be bigger than life?

576 If you could be an explorer, what would be your expedition?

577 What do you love about the internet?

578 Who was the last person to knock/ring at your door?

579 Where is your ideal place to raise kids or start a family?

580 Do you make choices on what's best for you or what's easiest?

581 Did you ever sneak out of your house after curfew without your parents knowing?

582 What topic do you always give your two cents on?

583 Do you prefer blue or black inked pens?

584 What gives you wanderlust?

585 What is your favorite short story?

586 Do you read other people's body language and if so does it help?

587 What is your favorite "take out" place?

588 Have you ever lied your way out of a bad situation, what?

589 What do you always lose track of besides time?

590 What strange thing would you like to happen at your funeral to make people laugh?

591 What is your favorite pancake or waffle topping?

592 What is your most favorite decorative piece or artwork you own?

593 How much money would make you happy?

594 What famous person's memoire would you love to read?

595 Would you rather give your money or time to a charity?

596 When you die, do you want to be buried or cremated?

597 Are you a clean or messy person?

598 You're auctioning yourself off for charity, why would someone pay big dollars for you?

599 Describe 2 funny traits about your dad.

600 When should you reveal a secret that you promised you wouldn't reveal?

601 What do you think is the biggest sign of a weakness in a person?

602 What potential talents do you think you might have if you worked at them?

603 How could you expand on your creative abilities?

604 Have you ever owned a goldfish?

605 Have you ever tried online dating, why/why not?

606 If your life were a commercial, what would your commercial jingle say?

607 What do you love to do for "me time?"

608 If someone assigned you a random job to start, what's the worst career for you?

609 Do you do your utmost for the environment?

610 Do you say curse words, if so which one do you use the most?

611 Worst leader in history, in your opinion?

612 What is your biggest debt right now?

613 Would you ever consider living in Iceland?

614 If you had to open up a lemonade stand tomorrow, what would you call your stand?

615 Do you believe in coincidences?

616   What eats up most of your time that you'd like to change?

617   What do you feel connected to?

618   How blunt are you and what is the boldest thing you've said to someone?

619   What thing that you've made are you most proud of?

620   Do you like your significant other's friends, why or why not?

621   Have you ever felt like a hamster on a wheel never getting anywhere? Why?

622   Do you have a chip on your shoulder about something?

623   What is that one thing your friends or family never let you live down?

624   What word or phrase do you say too much?

625   How did your parents meet?

626   What was something that happened to you as a kid that still scares you today?

627   If you had to attend a military boot camp, rename it based on your current fitness level.

628   Do you have any subscriptions?

629   What is your kryptonite?

630   Do you believe in the validity of IQ tests?

631 Have you ever been scuba diving?

632 If you have to be handcuffed to someone for 24 hours, who would it be?

633 Give your funniest answer to: "why did the chicken cross the road?"

634 What have you read online recently that inspired you?

635 Compare your writing style to any published author.

636 Will you still celebrate your birthday the older you get?

637 What do you have a love/hate relationship with?

638 Where is your favorite place to meditate?

639 What do you think is the biggest violation of privacy?

640 What crime would you like to investigate?

641 When you were a kid did you ever ask Santa for anything, if so what?

642 Have you ever been kicked out of anything, if so what?

643 Who was your first crush?

644 What inspires you to be a better person?

645 What is one subscription you don't want to live without?

646 Could you ever be a mortician if it paid really well and you needed a job?

647 Describe war in your opinion in just a few words.

648 How good is your willpower? Typically what do you use it for?

649 What is the most despicable thing about politics?

650 How many pairs of shoes do you own?

651 Have you ever walked out of a cinema before the film was done?

652 What makes you vulnerable?

653 A secret you've been wanting to share.

654 What is something you've gotten a second opinion on?

655 If you could collaborate on a rap with one rapper, who would it be?

656 What is the cleverest way you ever asked for someone's phone number?

657 What is your favorite smell/scent?

658 What is your favorite popcorn topping?

659 What are you really intense with?

660 What do you make way more complicated than it has to be?

661 Have you ever ridden a mechanical bull, or would you?

662 Have you ever been in a submarine?

663 How do you march to the beat of your own drum?

664 Which song do you hate the most?

665 Where do you lack discipline in your life?

666 What is one thing you do you consider practical?

667 If you were in charge, what 3 items would you have in the office vending machine?

668 Do you trust people that don't look you in the eye?

669 Are you an introvert or extrovert?

670 Do you have in-laws, if so do you get along with them?

671 Do you act different around a certain person, if so who?

672 What does your typical breakfast look like?

673 Have you ever tried to change anybody, if so who?

674 Have you ever had a dream you chased only to be let down when you achieved it?

675 Do you prefer texting or talking on the phone?

676 How old do you feel?

677 If you were to get a tattoo tomorrow what would it be?

678 Do you have any family secrets?

679 What is your favorite activity or way to workout (even if it's a small amount)?

680 Who do you seek most for advice?

681 Would you work less and do more of the things you enjoy if it meant you had less money?

682 Do you think street smarts count for anything?

683 If you saw someone drop a $10 bill, would you keep it or try to return it?

684 If you could be a host for a day would you host a game show, award show or what?

685 Would you be open to preserving your body through cryogenics?

686 Do you like scary movies?

687 What is your most embarrassing moment in public?

688 How do you cheer up a friend?

689 In what way are you neurotic?

690 Have you ever sucked on a lemon?

691 What is the last thing you took a picture of?

692 How are you always or ever evolving, what specific thing do you do?

693 When you were in school who was your favorite essay or assignment about?

694 How important is physical fitness to you?

695 How close are you to your family?

696 If you broke down on the side of the road could you change your own tire without help?

697 Who or what has been your best teacher?

698 Do you support local businesses in your community, if so what's your favorite?

699 How sensitive are you?

700 Do you have a favorite uplifting self-help book that encourages you?

701 If you were asked to create a column like "Dear Abby" what would you call it?

702 Have you ever felt trapped, if so when?

703 Do you like comic books, if so what's your favorite?

704 What have you been very lucky at?

705 Where is your favorite place to take a walk?

706 What word do you have the hardest time spelling?

707 Have you ever played Sudoku, and on a scale of 1-10 (10=expert) how good are you?

708 What's your most expensive piece of clothing?

709 What's your favorite saying?

710 If you started your own podcast what would it be about and what's the title?

711 How impulsive are you and what are you most impulsive with?

712 Have you ever overheard someone saying something negative about you? What was it?

713 What makes you feel like a kid again?

714 If you were entering a world like *Star Wars* would you be a Jedi or Sith?

715 The biggest jerk you've ever met.

716 What is the most serious issue facing the planet right now?

717 What wild animal deserves our protection?

718 Is there something in life you'd never give up for anyone?

719 Is there a reoccurring theme in your life?

720 What's the best independent film you've ever seen?

721 What restores your faith in humanity?

722 Are you afraid of dying, if so how do you cope?

723 If you were joining the *Star Wars* cast as a Jedi, what would be your Jedi name?

724 Are you psychic in any way?

725 What is your favorite breed of dog?

726 What is your preferred playing piece in *Monopoly?*

727 What was the one most important thing you learned from your parents?

728 What is the biggest piece of wisdom you think our elders can offer?

729 Have you ever given someone bad advice? If so what did you say?

730 Are you a bad loser or a good sport?

731 What quality or trait do you possess that could make people see you as a warrior?

732 What is one thing people buy that you think is a total waste of money?

733 What was your last big achievement?

734 When playing a game of charades, what would be the most fun to act out?

735 Do you like the "craft" food and drink movement, what specific craft items do you love?

736   Did you apply to or win any scholarships, if so what kind?

737   What keeps you balanced in life and work?

738   If you could steal one thing without consequence what would it be?

739   Are you reliable?

740   If you were on death row what would be your last meal?

741   What can people count on you for?

742   Are you any good at giving massages?

743   How many times have you had your heart broken?

744   If you were going to be a famous artist, who would be your muse?

745   Do you try to learn something new every day?

746   What is your favorite party game?

747   Do you think smiles are contagious and do you smile more than not?

748   What could someone use to bribe you?

749   Are you a registered voter and if so do you vote in every election?

750   What or who do you feel has attempted a "hostile takeover" of your life metaphorically?

$1 OFF
Any Grande or larger Starbucks or Teavana Handcrafted Beverage

Visit the Cafe between 7/1/19 and
7/31/19 and save $1 off any 1 Grande,
Venti or Trenta Handcrafted Beverage.
NOT VALID ON BOTTLED OR NON-HANDCRAFTED
CANNOT COMBINE WITH 7/8-7/21 FRAPP PROMO

To redeem: Present this coupon in the Cafe

W7V3K4F

This coupon may be redeemed only once per
customer at participating B&N Cafe
locations. Eligible Teavana beverages are
Chai Latte or Iced Teas with lemonade only.

seller's return policy... eBooks, digital downloads, and used books are not returnable or exchangeable. Defective NOOKs may be exchanged at the store in accordance with the applicable warranty.

Returns or exchanges will not be permitted (i) after 14 days or without receipt or (ii) for product not carried by Barnes & Noble or Barnes & Noble.com.

Policy on receipt may appear in two sections.

Return Policy

With a sales receipt or Barnes & Noble.com packing slip, a full refund in the original form of payment will be issued from any Barnes & Noble Booksellers store for returns of undamaged NOOKs, new and unread books, and unopened and undamaged music CDs, DVDs, vinyl records, toys/games and audio books made within 14 days of purchase from a Barnes & Noble Booksellers store or Barnes & Noble.com with the below exceptions.

A store credit for the purchase price will be issued (i) for purchases made by check less than 7 days prior to the date of return, (ii) when a gift receipt is presented within 60 days of purchase, (iii) for textbooks, (iv) when the original tender is PayPal, or (v) for products purchased at Barnes & Noble College bookstores that are listed for sale in the Barnes & Noble Booksellers inventory management system.

Opened music CDs, DVDs, vinyl records, audio books may not be returned, and can be exchanged only for the same title and only if defective. NOOKs purchased from other retailers or sellers are returnable only to the retailer or seller from which they are purchased, pursuant to such retailer's or seller's return policy. Magazines, newspapers, eBooks, digital downloads, and used books are not returnable or exchangeable. Defective NOOKs may be exchanged at the store in accordance with the

751   What is your idea of relaxing?

752   Are you financially responsible or do you still have problems managing money?

753   Have you ever attended a book reading, if so what book?

754   Do you have an incident from college you wish you could erase?

755   The biggest misconception.

756   What is your favorite joke?

757   Where can you find the best view in your city?

758   What is the longest book you've ever read?

759   What do you hate about the internet?

760   Do you consider yourself a nature lover?

761   Describe one undeniable fact about yourself.

762   What's the toughest decision you've made this year?

763   What is your favorite fruit?

764   If you were going to start your own clothing line, what would you name it?

765   Are you a gossip?

766   Do you ever laugh at things you shouldn't?

767   What's the most expensive thing you own?

768   What do you think airlines should offer on flights that they currently do not?

769   What is meaningful to you?

770   Do you have any music on vinyl or cassettes?

771   What gives you the creeps?

772   Do you think it's good to take it one day at a time?

773   Do you think flying is safe or do you have reservations?

774   What's the biggest lie you once believed was true?

775   What was the hardest goodbye you ever had?

776   Do you know how many kids you want if any and do you want boys or girls?

777   What is one thing in your life you can't make a decision on?

778   Have you ever ridden a camel?

779   Have you ever had a facial, if so, how'd it make you feel?

780   Would you ever turn in a family member if they broke the law?

781   What gets you excited about life?

782   Do you have a favorite thing you do for "girls/guys night out"?

783   Have you ever tried to be something you weren't, if so what?

784   Would you still buy a desktop computer or do you consider them obsolete?

785   Do you believe in aliens?

786   What is the last meal you cooked for someone?

787   What one thing does your mom do that makes you laugh?

788   How do you feel about redheads?

789   What is the smartest investment you've ever made?

790   What TV sitcom (past or present) best represents your family?

791   Do you think schools need more physical activities versus activities to resolve conflict?

792   What is something you hate but wished you loved?

793   What is one thing you failed at many times but kept trying until you finally succeeded?

794   How do you like to preserve memories?

795   Have you ever been on a cable car?

796 What is the main thing that influences your decisions?

797 If you were going to write a children's book, what would the story be about?

798 What was the first responsibility your parents gave you as a kid?

799 What stood out in one of your most memorable dreams?

800 What would you do if someone proposed to you tomorrow?

801 What magazine would you like to be on the cover of?

802 What do you think you'd be good at selling?

803 What is the biggest high pressure situation you've ever found yourself in?

804 What is your weirdest trait?

805 Can you name all 50 state capitals in the U.S.?

806 If you invented a monster what would you call it and what would it look like?

807 What's the most recent self-discovery you uncovered?

808 What do you like to eat with your sandwich (soup, fries, or something else)?

809 Would you rather play golf or go fishing?

810 Do you have a favorite Prince song?

811   What is your favorite word beginning with the letter X?

812   What's the most embarrassing thing your parents did to you as a kid?

813   Have you ever colored in an adult coloring book, did you like it?

814   What is one thing college freshmen should be prepared for?

815   Have you ever been in a newspaper?

816   What is your favorite trivia game?

817   Name one thing you could do to become a modern day Robin Hood?

818   Has anyone ever said "I love you" and you couldn't say it back?

819   What was some of the best news you ever received?

820   Who is the most philanthropic person you know and who do they give to?

821   Is your bellybutton an innie or outie?

822   Do you believe in one best friend or just friends?

823   What vegetable do you hate?

824   What is the worst pickup line you've heard?

825   If you had to pick one food to eat every day for the rest of your life, what would it be?

826 Have you ever burned a bridge on purpose and how do you feel about that now?

827 What law do you think should be more of a personal choice, instead of a law?

828 Do you have a favorite YouTube channel, what is it?

829 The most annoying bill you have to pay?

830 Your secret obsession.

831 What is the scariest insect you can think of?

832 What hobby or activity do you think is totally boring that other people enjoy?

833 What one thing could you easily live without?

834 Do you think there is life after death?

835 A memory you think of often.

836 What is one thing if you ever lost it would devastate you?

837 Do you believe in "don't let the sun set on your anger," meaning don't go to bed angry?

838 Are you a convincing liar or can people see through you?

839 What video game do you wish life were more like?

840 Do you think it's more important to love or be loved?

841 What is something children of today are not doing enough of?

842 What has been the worst decision you've made in your life so far?

843 Coke or Pepsi?

844 How good are you at fixing things and what specifically are you handy at?

845 What was the last social faux pas you made?

846 What do you think there is a "war on" in today's society?

847 What celebrity makes you want to scream (in a bad way)?

848 Do you have an expansive vocabulary?

849 If you had to create chapters in your diary or journal, name 3 chapters.

850 What do you do when you want to get out of your own head?

851 What's the funniest movie you've ever seen?

852 Have you ever been called a troublemaker, if so by who?

853 What is something in life you really have an appreciation for that most people don't?

854 Which was the greatest empire?

855 Has anyone ever blackmailed you, and how?

856   Do you give your opinion and feedback on surveys?

857   Have you ever been in a tug of war? Did you win?

858   What do you hate the monotony of?

859   What is your favorite flower?

860   Do you think a stay at home mom works just as hard as a career woman?

861   Are you a lover or a fighter?

862   If you were a stand-up comedian, who do you know would give you the most material?

863   What or who has made the biggest impression on your life in the last year?

864   Do you bite your nails?

865   How do you feel about nepotism?

866   How much would it cost to buy your love?

867   How often do you laugh?

868   What instrument do you know how to play?

869   Are you good at keeping secrets?

870   What is something quirky you find attractive in a person?

871   If you were a wrestler what would your stage name and special move be?

872   Use one word to describe your confidence level.

873   What's the best Valentine's Day gift you've ever given/received?

874   Have you ever had a stuffed toy important to you, if so what kind and what was its name?

875   Who was your very first celebrity crush on?

876   Do you think any kind of afterlife exists?

877   What is your favorite chick flick or romcom movie?

878   What is one thing you won't admit to yourself?

879   What question do you want to ask the universe?

880   Have you ever been somewhere you thought was haunted, if so where?

881   What has made you feel completely validated?

882   Have you ever done something and had no idea why you did it, what was it?

883   Do you stick to conventional fashion or like to be original?

884   What appetizer do you have to eat when you dine out?

885   Out of all the feelings you can feel, what is the best feeling in the world?

886 There were two nature channel shows on mermaids. Do you think they could exist?

887 Do you give money to homeless people you see on the street?

888 What is your least favorite personality trait you like about yourself?

889 What have you considered interning for?

890 What is your favorite way to spend a Sunday?

891 If you could have a child with a famous person, who would it be and for what reason?

892 Do you think the guy should always pay? What about on the first date?

893 What novel would you love to be transported into to live out your days?

894 What do you think about the "tiny house" craze and is it for you?

895 When you meet a new person do you like to talk about yourself or prefer to let them talk?

896 What is the coolest nickname you've ever heard for someone?

897 How good are you at trivia questions and what trivia subject would you excel at?

898 Would you kill an innocent person if you thought it might mean saving a dozen others?

899 What's your favorite way to waste time?

900 Do you regret going or not going to college?

901 If a genie offered you three wishes, what would you wish for (not more wishes)?

902 What housework/chore do you absolutely refuse to do?

903 Name something you had a close call with?

904 If you could live one week with an uncivilized tribe to learn their ways, would you?

905 What one thing are you worried will never change for you?

906 How do you resolve conflict?

907 If you were going to write an essay about your life what would your essay be called?

908 Do you think there should be a salary cap for actors in movies?

909 Do you have a favorite furniture designer, if so who?

910 What is your favorite outfit?

911 What is your point of no return?

912 Are you a godparent to a child, if so whose?

913 What did you think was stupid until you tried it?

914 Would you ever date someone with a kid or kids?

915 What is the worst thing you've ever tried?

916 Who is the most interesting person you've ever met?

917 Would you try to eat vegan for a week or longer?

918 Would you say you're easy to get along with?

919 What is the most expensive thing you've ever broken?

920 Have you ever got majorly lost trying to get somewhere?

921 Could you ever go out with someone just because they're rich?

922 Do you know what an Arnold Palmer is and if so do you like it?

923 What is the fastest way to get you bored?

924 What is the bane of your existence?

925 What birthday do you feel is more of a landmark: 16th, 18th or 21st?

926 What is your favorite nursery rhyme?

927 Do you trust your coworkers?

928 What scares you the most about getting older?

929 What gives you peace of mind?

930 Can you tap dance?

931   Is there any one product that has changed your life in a good way?

932   Is there any experience you've not had that you regret not having yet?

933   What is your favorite Broadway show or one you really want to see?

934   What book do you think should be mandatory for everyone on the planet to read?

935   What do you think most people take for granted?

936   What do people take for granted that really bugs you?

937   Would you say you are a good or bad influence to others?

938   What is the most beautiful city in the world?

939   What is your favorite idiom?

940   If you were going on *Shark Tank* to pitch an idea, whom would you want to work with?

941   Have you made an impact on anyone's life, if so who?

942   What is your favorite band beginning with the letter Q?

943   What bad habits do you think kids pick up from their parents?

944   Do you have any cool party tricks?

945   What famous person has completely lost your respect?

946 Have you ever talked in your sleep and if not what would you be afraid to say?

947 What random act of kindness should be done every day?

948 Do you spend too much time pleasing others at a detriment to yourself?

949 Do you always wear identical socks?

950 Do you have any allergies, specifically to food that are serious?

951 What is the main thing you've always had second thoughts about?

952 What two celebrities would make the craziest couple you could think of?

953 Who do you think in general is smarter, men or women?

954 What is one thing you know about your mom or dad that they don't know you know?

955 What are a few things you need to cleanse from your life?

956 What is the craziest craving you ever had?

957 How organized are you?

958 Do you think cigarette smoking should be illegal?

959 What TV sitcom family (old or new) would you have liked to be a member of?

960 What was your most creative endeavor?

961 Have you ever walked out of a restaurant or bar without paying your bill, if so why?

962 What's the best thing about being a part of your family?

963 Have you ever been a big brother or sister to a less fortunate youth, would you?

964 How do you feel about your family?

965 When you were a kid did you have any posters on your wall, if so of what?

966 What is something you're teased about relentlessly?

967 What is the biggest city you've ever been to?

968 What do you think the most romantic proposal looks like?

969 What is your favorite thing to BBQ?

970 Do desperate times call for desperate measures?

971 What are you too hard on yourself about?

972 Would you fight for the one you love or would you just let them go?

973 Do you prefer movies with or without special effects?

974 How jealous are you when it comes to your significant other?

975 If evil-doers invaded your country would you rush to the battle lines or hide?

976   What is the nicest thing a stranger has ever done for you?

977   If you were a woman would you propose to a man? If you were a man would you accept it?

978   Where would you never live?

979   What would be the best exotic pet?

980   Is there a food you loved as a kid but hate as an adult?

981   Have you ever rescued an animal, if so did you keep it or take it to a shelter?

982   Do you have a favorite news anchor, if so who?

983   What is your favorite metaphor?

984   Would you ever set up a nanny cam to spy on someone watching your kids?

985   How many back up plans do you make for your original plan?

986   How do you feel about people wearing animal furs and animal skinned shoes?

987   Would you ever date someone much older or younger than you, and which?

988   What do you do to cool down when it's hot out?

989   Would you ever allow yourself to be auctioned off for a good cause or charity?

990   What is the funniest one liner joke you've ever told?

991   What do most people consider a weakness that you actually find strength in?

992   Have you done something you worry could come back to haunt you, what?

993   Should graduating high school be mandatory?

994   What is the most important thing in your life right now?

995   What are you hypocritical about?

996   Do you like racing events like cars, horse or dog and if so what is your favorite?

997   Do you watch football, if so do you have any special "game day" rituals?

998   What animal do you think is jaw dropping beautiful?

999   How often do you self-reflect?

1000   What would you ask King Henry VIII if you could have dinner with him?

1001   Do you like to cuddle?

1002   Have you ever danced in the rain?

1003   Who or what challenges you?

1004   Have you ever hid anything from your significant other that you wanted to tell them?

1005   Would you consider yourself worldly?

1006 What song makes you sad the moment you hear it?

1007 What is the closest thing to your superpower?

1008 What is the scariest thing you've ever done?

1009 What is your favorite film beginning with the letter L?

1010 In any of your relationships what was one of the hardest challenges you faced?

1011 Biggest risk you've ever taken.

1012 If you were a stranger looking at your life from the outside in, would it inspire you?

1013 What major scientific advancement do you predict will be released in the next 20 years?

1014 Do you let other people's negativity effect you?

1015 What issue has ever divided your family or a specific relationship?

1016 Have you ever shoved things in the closet to make your room look clean?

1017 What type of journalist would you be?

1018 Have you ever starred in an amateur or professional video?

1019 What was the worst way you've been dumped or dumped someone else?

1020 What do you daydream about?

1021   Have you ever gotten lost in a maze?

1022   Have you ever sworn at an authority figure?

1023   Do you think people are basically bad or basically good?

1024   Have you ever shamed anyone and if so what for?

1025   If you wrote an autobiography what would your book be called?

1026   What is one thing you hope to do before you die?

1027   Do you prefer to wash up in the mornings or evenings?

1028   What was a game changer in your life?

1029   Are you a realist or do you like to lose touch with reality sometimes?

1030   What fashion style would you like to bring back?

1031   What is the biggest obstacle you've had to overcome?

1032   When you think about the future what one word comes to mind?

1033   Who do you think has the best smile?

1034   What is the most interesting thing you can see out of your nearest window?

1035   Do you have a high level of curiosity, and has it hurt or helped you?

1036 Who is your favorite TV talk show host past or present?

1037 What is one thing you hate about computers?

1038 Have you ever Googled yourself or a family member?

1039 What brand or product do you buy because you feel it's trustworthy?

1040 If you discovered a new species of dinosaur what would you call it?

1041 How many times a day do you check your Facebook?

1042 Do you think regular (not cable) TV shows has too much inappropriate content?

1043 If you designed your own sushi roll what would be in it and its name?

1044 If you could have any feature from an animal what would you want?

1045 Who have you learned the most from?

1046 Finish this sentence as if it were your life: "It was a dark and stormy night..."

1047 If you were a fashion designer, what style of clothing or accessories would you design?

1048 What do you think of non-profit organizations that pay their CEOs using donated funds?

1049 Something you were accused of that you never did.

1050 You've been given money to purchase a major sports team, what team will you buy?

1051 What's the grossest thing you've ever seen someone do in public?

1052 What is the first thing people usually notice about you?

1053 Do you believe in miracles, have you had one?

1054 The oddest job you ever took to earn a buck?

1055 In past publicized criminal cases, who was "not guilty" that you would have convicted?

1056 What do you love on your burger or veggie burger?

1057 Did you ever fail a subject in school, if so what class?

1058 What is something constant in your life?

1059 Have you ever conducted an experiment that went awry, if so what?

1060 Name your alter ego.

1061 Where is somewhere you really want to visit but you worry you won't eat the food?

1062 What benefit do you think employees should get that most companies don't offer?

1063 If you were on the run from law enforcement what country would you flee to?

1064 What is the biggest challenge kids face today?

1065 Have you ever taken part in a parade, if so why and what did you do?

1066 Have you ever made someone cry?

1067 Can you solve a Rubik's cube?

1068 What is the most artistic thing you've ever done?

1069 What would your friends say about you?

1070 What was the hardest test you've ever taken and did you have to take it over?

1071 What blood type do you have?

1072 What is your favorite game beginning with the letter N?

1073 When was the last time you felt lucky?

1074 Have you ever been bitten or attacked by an animal, if so what and why?

1075 What movie ending really frustrated you? And how would you change it?

1076 Have you ever had anything waxed, if so what?

1077 What is one thing you'll never be associated with?

1078 What makes someone a bad kisser in your opinion?

1079 Are you too critical of other people and has it ever effected a relationship?

1080 If you had unlimited space or room in your home, what would you use it for?

1081   What keeps you going?

1082   What topic would you be totally clueless about if it came up in a conversation?

1083   Do you have a piggy bank?

1084   What type of people scare you?

1085   What is your favorite spa service (massage, facial, etc....)?

1086   How do you handle two-faced people?

1087   Who would call you their biggest cheerleader?

1088   Do you have a specific personality trait or something specific that makes you popular?

1089   If you could be reincarnated as an animal, what animal would you choose?

1090   Do you think the glass ceiling still exists or has it finally been broken?

1091   What do you want to do when you retire?

1092   What is something that intrigues you and scares you at the same time?

1093   Do you watch any nature programs, if so which ones?

1094   What is the largest amount of money you've spent in one spree?

1095   Would you ever pick up a hitchhiker?

1096　How do you deal with shallow people?

1097　What was your happiest dream about?

1098　Who is your favorite superhero?

1099　What compulsions do you have?

1100　Can you build a house of cards?

1101　Do you often have a tune in your head you can't name?

1102　Has someone ever been promoted over you who you felt was not qualified for the job?

1103　What is the definition of a soul to you in a few words?

1104　If you could go on an adventure tomorrow, what adventure would you choose?

1105　How do you feel about fracking in a few words?

1106　Would you rather swim in a pool or the ocean?

1107　Are you possessive, if so how much?

1108　What are your top 3 bloggers/blog sites to read?

1109　What's the most sensible thing you've ever heard someone say?

1110　Chess or Checkers?

1111   If you were a villain or criminal mastermind what would be your calling card?

1112   Are you a good aim with a rubber band?

1113   What was your parents' greatest sacrifice?

1114   Do you think in this day and age investing in the stock market is wise?

1115   Have you ever been electrocuted?

1116   What color annoys you when you see it?

1117   If you were a chicken, why would you cross the road?

1118   What is/was the best thing about being in a relationship?

1119   What keeps you optimistic?

1120   Have you ever turned something valuable someone lost in or kept it?

1121   What's one chore or task you love doing?

1122   If you could create a fantasy land what is one thing it would have in it?

1123   What tests your patience?

1124   If you could talk to one species of animal what would it be?

1125   Are you still close with any of your early childhood friends, and who?

1126 Do you take the time to listen to what others have to say?

1127 What is your most favorite way to receive affection?

1128 If a waiter spilled a drink on you but it was an accident, would you still tip?

1129 What are you allergic to?

1130 What is one thing you wish you could change about your family?

1131 Are you a positive person?

1132 What is your favorite song beginning with the letter I?

1133 Have you ever read a tabloid, if so which one?

1134 Have you ever been fired and if so from where?

1135 Have you ever test driven a car you couldn't afford, if so what car?

1136 Have you ever staged an intervention and for what?

1137 Many people read electronic books. Do you think that takes away from the experience?

1138 Have you ever invented a fairly unique meal or drink?

1139 Have you ever gotten back into a relationship with an ex, if so did it work out?

1140 Is external or internal beauty more important to you?

1141 What is your favorite dessert?

1142 Are you more of a leader or follower?

1143 What is harmonious in your life?

1144 What keeps you busy most days?

1145 Do you think all is fair in love and war?

1146 What's the most radical thing you've done appearance wise?

1147 How do you feel about growing older?

1148 What is the meaning of life?

1149 What celebrity's crib would you love to take a tour of?

1150 How can you live with more intention?

1151 Do you brood about anything?

1152 Do you prefer to wear shoes or go barefoot, why?

1153 What is the most expensive gift you've ever bought for someone?

1154 Have you ever run for an election, if so what was your campaign?

1155 What makes a person victorious?

1156   What has been the best decision you've made in your life so far?

1157   Have you ever been attracted to someone your best friend was dating?

1158   What causes you deep emotional pain when you think about it?

1159   What do you consider is the most important piece of furniture in a house?

1160   What "new beginning" are you most looking forward to?

1161   If you personalize your car's license plate, what would the plate say?

1162   What is your favorite mix of salty and sweet?

1163   If your parents hated your partner you loved, would you listen to them and break it off?

1164   Have you ever practiced origami?

1165   Do you believe in ghosts?

1166   If you ruled your own country, who would you get to write your national anthem?

1167   Are you a giver or a receiver?

1168   Something you always over exaggerate.

1169   Best advice you've ever been given?

1170   Would you ever spend the night on the beach?

1171   What was your favorite bedtime story as a child?

1172   Do you have a propensity for anything?

1173   Have you ever been wheelbarrow racing?

1174   If you were a going to be a wedding singer, what would your stage name be?

1175   What is your favorite kind of puzzle?

1176   Do you believe everyone deserves a second chance?

1177   What is your favorite cartoon character beginning with the letter W?

1178   What is the most enjoyable thing your family has done with you?

1179   Have you ever been alienated, if so from what?

1180   Something you keep close to your heart.

1181   Have you ever built a snowman?

1182   You're falling through the rabbit hole, what's on the other side?

1183   Have you ever felt like you were being stalked and if so how?

1184   What food do you love but gives you a bad reaction or is too hard for you to eat?

1185   Have you ever gone bird watching?

1186   Do prefer to live in the heart of the city or out in the peaceful countryside?

1187   What do you think is the scariest thing about becoming a parent?

1188   If you could try out a job for a day just to see if you like it, what job would you choose?

1189   What one thing could you do a little better every day?

1190   Have you ever hit rock bottom?

1191   Who is your biggest supporter?

1192   If a reality TV show were based around your life what would it be called?

1193   Are you a hat person?

1194   Do you like your age?

1195   What particular field of study were you really interested in, but decided not to pursue?

1196   What industry do you think is most harmful to the planet or environment?

1197   What do you like on your toast or biscuit?

1198   Would you allow a foreign exchange student to live in your house?

1199   Have your parents told you something as an adult they kept from you as a child?

1200   If you were going to call a family meeting, what topic would it be about?

1201   *Harry Potter* or *Lord of the Rings*, which story is best to you?

1202   What makes you feel unsafe?

1203   Do you consider yourself to be high maintenance?

1204   What do you find ethereal?

1205   What is the kindest thing you've done for a stranger?

1206   How many countries have you visited?

1207   Would you ever let your parents pick out a partner for you?

1208   What movie or book ending really left you hanging to the point of anger?

1209   What distracts you the most every day?

1210   Given the chance would you work from home or do you love working with others?

1211   Have you ever judged a book by its cover?

1212   What 3 wishes would you grant the world?

1213   Have you ever lied to get a promotion or anything else?

1214   If you had to dedicate the rest of your life to a cause, what would that be?

1215   What do you think about men who want to be a stay at home dad?

1216　Can you stand on your hands unassisted?

1217　Are you being true to yourself?

1218　Can you easily move forward after a hurt?

1219　What one trait do you have that will make you a terrible boss?

1220　What animal do you think should be added to the endangered species list?

1221　What do you do when you get a "gut" feeling about something?

1222　What was the last thing to make you feel happy?

1223　Do you think it's important for a wife to take her husband's last name?

1224　What's your biggest challenge in the mornings?

1225　What is the next biggest step in your life?

1226　Have you ever spied on anyone via social media?

1227　What games do people play that drive you crazy or get on your nerves?

1228　Do you share a bond with someone, if so who?

1229　What makes technology useful to you?

1230　Do you think libraries are still useful?

1231   How old were you when you last went trick or treating?

1232   Have you ever played golf?

1233   Would you rather be a jack-of-all trades or master of one?

1234   Do you prefer male or female singers' voices?

1235   Have you tried something completely unorthodox that was supposed to be healthy?

1236   Have you ever been in a position of authority?

1237   Do you celebrate the things you have?

1238   What or who keeps you grounded?

1239   Have you ever been sledding?

1240   In your opinion who was the worst President of the United States?

1241   Are you familiar with *Robert's Rules of Order* and if so do you agree?

1242   Did anyone in your family have a "home remedy" and what did it cure?

1243   If you were playing a game of truth or dare, what dare would you be afraid to attempt?

1244   How good is your balance and could you balance on a tightrope with practice?

1245   Have you met a real life warrior, if so who?

1246　What temptation can you not resist?

1247　When you get stuck on bed rest what do you do to pass time?

1248　Do you move a lot?

1249　What is your special song?

1250　How sociable are you in new group settings?

1251　What's your favorite time of the year?

1252　Who is the best playwright in your opinion?

1253　What is your favorite way to start your day?

1254　What is the worst name you've ever called anyone?

1255　If you had to take superhero sides are you Marvel or DC?

1256　Do you believe in fate or that a person shapes their own destiny?

1257　When getting ready for a party, what takes you forever?

1258　Do you still have feelings for an ex that have never gone away?

1259　Are you ok going out alone or do you prefer to have company?

1260　What is one thing you'd change about the current city you live in now?

1261   Have you ever been bobbing for apples?

1262   What is the longest road trip you've ever done in a car so far, where'd you go?

1263   What have been accused of being irrational about?

1264   Do you need to write down things to remember them?

1265   Have you ever sailed a boat?

1266   Who is the most drama filled person you know, and what do they do?

1267   Have you ever had a run in with the law and if so what for?

1268   If ketchup wasn't available, what would you like to dip your fries in?

1269   Are you good at owning your mistakes?

1270   What do you think about the sound of your voice and what do you think you sound like?

1271   What was the last book you read, sum it up in one word?

1272   What question are you too embarrassed to ask anyone?

1273   What is your favorite type of tree?

1274   What game show do you think you'd win the most money on?

1275   How would you describe your decorating style in a few simple terms?

1276 What is your biggest weakness?

1277 How do you personally feel about gambling of any kind?

1278 Have you ever given blood?

1279 What do you usually have to improvise on?

1280 What monument do you think should not have been erected?

1281 Have you ever put a part of your life on hold, what part?

1282 Pick a title of a novel to describe your love life.

1283 Do you have a green thumb?

1284 Who is your favorite comedian?

1285 Would you ever consider living on an island, why or why not?

1286 If there were aliens in the universe, what would you say to them?

1287 Do you believe change is a good thing?

1288 If a tree falls in the forest and there's no one around to hear it does it make a sound?

1289 Name one infamous person you actually like and want to hang out with.

1290 Have you ever tossed your own pancake?

1291 What gift would be awkward to receive from your boss?

1292 Have you ever walked a tightrope?

1293 Do you usually say what's on your mind or do you hold back?

1294 What is something you just can't relate to?

1295 Your biggest "what if?"

1296 What is a growing concern of yours?

1297 Has someone ever given you a second chance, if so how?

1298 What flavor icecream do you hate?

1299 What do you think all kindergarten students should learn?

1300 Do you have a kind of un-special talent you're really good at?

1301 What was the most generous act of your life so far?

1302 Are your expectations of other people realistic or too high?

1303 When have you ever really scared yourself?

1304 If you had to be handcuffed to someone for 24 hours, who would it be?

1305 When did you first realize that life is short?

1306 What is your perfect weekend getaway?

1307 Where are your ancestors from?

1308 Who was the last person you hand wrote a letter to?

1309 You've just been invited to tour the White House, what are you most looking forward to?

1310 Do you ever feel blue and if so what triggers it?

1311 What 3 things would you never do on vacation?

1312 Do you keep a journal and does it help you?

1313 Has your ego ever gotten in the way of work or a relationship?

1314 Would you ever consider adopting a child?

1315 Who would you want to spend the last day of your life with?

1316 Have you ever felt discriminated against, if so how?

1317 What's the longest you've ever grown your hair?

1318 What instance did you not take "no" for an answer?

1319 Do you like other people buying you clothes?

1320 Would you rather be hated or forgotten?

1321   What is usually your first thought when you wake up?

1322   What is the earliest memory you have of your childhood?

1323   Has your life ever flashed before your eyes, if so what made it happen?

1324   Would you rather ask permission or apologize later?

1325   Do you have any phobias?

1326   If you had the opportunity to get a message across to a large group, what would it be?

1327   What is your favorite scent of candle or room spray?

1328   What is the most important thing you ever forgot?

1329   Where is the strangest place you've ever fallen asleep?

1330   Who can you impersonate really well?

1331   What one skill or trait do you feel is imperative to be successful?

1332   If your local newspaper were running a story on your life, what would the headline say?

1333   What makes a party boring?

1334   Would you ever raise your own chickens for fresh eggs?

1335   What keeps you on pins and needles?

1336   What is your favorite part of the day?

1337   Do you have a Swiss army knife?

1338   If you were to enter food-eating contest what would you want the food to be?

1339   What is one thing you wish you had the money to pay someone to do for you?

1340   Have you ever been pulled over by a cop, if so what were you doing?

1341   Is there a role in your life you feel very honored to have?

1342   In one sentence, how would you describe your relationship with your mother?

1343   Where and who was your first live concert?

1344   How would you explain your basic life philosophy?

1345   How would you describe your attention to detail?

1346   Do you think laughing at someone else's misfortune is wrong?

1347   What was the hardest thing you ever had to make peace with?

1348   What used to scare you as a child?

1349   Would you risk your life to save someone, if so who?

1350   What is the biggest and most elaborate lie you've ever told?

1351 What is something most people get wrong about you when they meet you?

1352 What opportunity do you wish you would have taken?

1353 Have you ever gotten food poisoning and if so what food gave it to you?

1354 What was your first job?

1355 What is your favorite part of the weekend?

1356 What is your favorite bedtime story?

1357 Where have you always wanted to have a birthday party?

1358 What is something that should be forbidden but is tolerated?

1359 Have you ever been bungee jumping? If not, do you want to?

1360 What is your favorite restaurant?

1361 In your opinion what's the best thing since sliced bread?

1365 What's your favorite website?

1363 Do you prefer baths or showers?

1364 What traffic laws or moving violations do you always seem to break?

1365 Have you ever been on a pogo stick?

1366   What's the biggest thing you need to improve?

1367   Are you comfortable learning new things, what was the last new thing you learned?

1368   What is your favorite mystery series?

1369   Describe what you want your retirement to feel like in one word?

1370   What do you and your friends do when you hang out?

1371   Are you supportive of a friend even if you don't agree with what they are doing?

1372   What is your favorite way to stay in shape?

1373   Who do you think is the most credible philosopher?

1374   Are you neat or messy?

1375   Do you think happiness is a choice?

1376   What has been your biggest sacrifice?

1377   What famous celebrity chef would you want to cater your dinner party?

1378   What is the longest movie you've ever watched?

1379   Do you like to travel?

1380   What do you think is not fair in today's society?

1381 If you decide to get cremated, where would you want your ashes spread?

1382 Who do you think you inspire?

1383 If someone asked you to give them a random piece of advice, what would you say?

1384 If there is hair in your food at a restaurant, what would you say?

1385 Describe your mood right now using one word.

1386 Does looking on the bright side help you?

1387 What is your first proper memory?

1388 What do you do if people are nosing into your business?

1389 Do you believe in taking leaps of faith?

1390 Who told you the best stories when you were a kid?

1391 If you were a flower, what type would you be?

1395 Do you have an unresolved ongoing family issue?

1393 If you had to create a children's book about an animal, what would your book be about?

1394 What sound relaxes you?

1395 Who do you think Jack the Ripper was?

1396   Do you think it's important for a couple getting married to share the same beliefs?

1397   What have you ever done out of spite?

1398   If you ever became a writer, what would be your writer's pseudonym?

1399   If you had to describe yourself as a flavor, what would it be?

1400   What is something too hard for you to imagine?

1401   Have you ever rescued anyone or anything?

1402   Do you think medical science is ahead of the times or behind?

1403   What is something you came close to giving up on?

1404   Would you rather trade some intelligence for looks or looks for intelligence?

1405   When do you function at your best?

1406   What is the first thing you reach for when you need comforting?

1407   Have you ever called in sick to work to do something more exciting, what was it?

1408   Have you ever had to rehearse anything, if so what?

1409   Do you watch any of the singing competitions, if so who is your favorite contestant?

1410   What is your favorite food to eat raw?

1411   If you could invent brand new baby names what would they be?

1412   What emotion is your least favorite and the one you are not in touch with?

1413   What celebrity do you think is a positive role model for kids today?

1414   Which do you like more: a really good book or a great movie?

1415   If you joined the circus what kind of performer would you be?

1416   If you participated tomorrow, could you win a spelling bee?

1417   What should wedding vows be about?

1418   Where was the last place you traveled to?

1419   Do you think there is life on other planets?

1420   Are you a trendsetter?

1421   Do you believe in destiny, fate or free will?

1422   If you could have anything named after you, what would you want it to be?

1423   What horror fiction character scares you the most?

1424   Do you think there is any merit to following feng shui in your home?

1425   How would you describe social media with one word or phrase?

1426   What was the brand of your first ever cell phone?

1427   What are your 3 favorite internet sites?

1428   Do you have a favorite pair of blue jeans? Describe them.

1429   What is standing between you and one of your biggest dreams?

1430   What profession do you respect?

1431   Have you ever been the recipient of a practical joke?

1432   Have you ever ate something you've dropped on the floor, if so what?

1433   Would you consider being an Uber driver if you needed to make extra money?

1434   How do you know when you're in love, what is the main sign?

1435   Have you ever gotten anything autographed, if so by who and what was it?

1436   Do you prefer Walmart or Target?

1437   What do you long for?

1438   If you could be a personal assistant to anyone, who would it be?

1439   What is the most important thing you can do to improve yourself?

1440   What makes it hard for you to keep your focus?

1441 Do you think society has become too PC (politically correct)?

1442 What tragic love story do you relate to?

1443 Has your intuition or "gut" served you well?

1444 What's the longest you've ever waited in line for something and what was it?

1445 Who is your favorite model?

1446 What have you done that is out of character for you?

1447 Would you rather get a gift card or a gift that shows the person shopped for you?

1448 Who is the most visionary person in your life and how do they inspire you?

1449 How do you handle a betrayal?

1450 What do you feel strong enough about to protest?

1451 What's the biggest blooper you've never lived down?

1452 If you owned a restaurant what kind of food would you want to serve?

1453 What will we find if we look in the bottom of your closet today?

1454 What kind of car did you learn how to drive on?

1455 What is the best thing you have done just because you were told you can't?

1456 Have you ever had to go to court or testify and if so what for?

1457 Are you more worried about doing things right, or doing the right things?

1458 What is the worst type of case for you to be on a jury where you would not be impartial?

1459 Do you believe in the term "Mother knows best"?

1460 Who is your favorite movie action hero?

1461 What is one thing you can get in your hometown that you can't get anywhere else?

1462 How important are looks in someone you're in a relationship with?

1463 What freedom do you feel is not really free anymore?

1464 What are you most thankful for?

1465 Do you have any favorite radio talk shows or talk radio programs that don't play music?

1466 What was the last book you read?

1467 What is your favorite online store?

1468 What band would you love to tour with and be a roadie for?

1469 If you were to throw a message in a bottle into the ocean, what would it say?

1470 Do you have common sense and do you think most people are lacking in it?

1471   What is your favorite non-alcoholic drink?

1472   What makes you feel rested and refreshed?

1473   If you could cast a spell on someone what spell would you cast and on who?

1474   What 3 songs will always be found at the top of your playlist?

1475   Do you keep a budget?

1476   What is the craziest thing you've ever done for someone?

1477   What is one thing you know about your family history you're proud of?

1478   What do you wait for discount sales to buy?

1479   What is priceless to you?

1480   What one thing in particular makes you feel good about yourself?

1481   Do you believe in karma?

1482   Have you ever been canoeing/kayaking?

1483   What do you think should require a mental health check before people are allowed to do?

1484   What do you like to put gravy on?

1485   How do you feel about thrift shops or flea markets?

1486   What was the funniest joke you ever heard about?

1487   Who depends on you the most?

1488   Do you prefer sporty or academic members of the opposite sex?

1489   Are you in favor of the death penalty?

1490   Do you have to experience something to fully understand it?

1491   Has anyone in your family ever served in the military?

1492   Do you think you could ever be a firefighter, why/why not?

1493   Finish the next line in your style: Roses are red, violets are blue…

1494   What embarrasses you instantly?

1495   What do you think there should be stiffer penalties for?

1496   Do you follow what your friends do with trends or are you your own trendsetter?

1497   Do you often read your horoscope?

1498   Do you have any scars?

1499   Are you more like your mom or your dad?

1500   What was the worst time you ever put your foot in your mouth and what did you say?

1501   Do you think athletes and actors are overpaid?

1502   If you were ruler of your own country what would you call it and what would be your title?

1503   Are you a daredevil?

1504   What current event are you tired of hearing about?

1505   Have you ever felt like something was missing in your life, if so do you know what it was?

1506   Do you think you could beat a lie detector test?

1507   Have you ever received a harsher punishment than you deserved for something you did?

1508   What song on your playlist gets played the most?

1509   Have you ever ridden on a train or subway and what did you like about it?

1510   Did you create a checklist for your ideal spouse, if so what were two things you wanted?

1511   Have you ever let your mom or significant other fight a battle for you?

1512   Has one of your biggest fears ever come true?

1513   Is there anything about the opposite sex you just don't understand or comprehend?

1514   What is one old thing in your life you've had since your youth, you just can't throw away?

1515   Could you ever be someone's bodyguard?

1516 What common pitfalls do you find yourself dealing with in your work life?

1517 Do you tend to follow your heart or your head?

1518 What celebrity or TV show in your opinion set a bad example for youth today?

1519 How do you feel about jazz music, if you like it who is your favorite?

1520 Have you ever been diagnosed with something that's challenged you, if so what?

1521 What is your favorite precious stone?

1522 If you had your perfect dream house, what kind of tree/s would you want in your yard?

1523 Describe your "poker face."

1524 If happiness were the national currency, what kind of work would make you rich?

1525 Do you keep up with current events, why or why not?

1526 Did you ever have a mean nickname that kids called you, one you didn't like?

1527 What childhood dreams have you neglected?

1528 Do you ever compare your life to anyone else's, if so who?

1529 What's the craziest thing you've done in a car?

1530 What's something weird you do before bedtime?

1531   What do you think should be censored?

1532   Are you related to anyone famous or historical, if so who?

1533   Would you ever donate a kidney to anyone, and who?

1534   How do you encourage yourself when you go through hard times?

1535   How are you different from most people?

1536   Have you ever fired a gun?

1537   What is the main quality you think makes a great parent?

1538   Do you think people, including yourself live up to their full potential?

1539   Have you ever stayed up for an entire 24 hours, why?

1540   What creature do you admire for its ability to adapt?

1541   Who is a female role model in your life?

1542   What was your biggest "Ah-ha!" moment or revelation?

1543   How do you feel about GMOs?

1544   Do you prefer popcorn or candy with your movie or something else?

1545   Have you ever asked yourself why you don't do the things you know you should be doing?

1546   How often do you reevaluate your life?

1547   What gives you a zest for life?

1548   What do you have trouble seeing clearly in your mind?

1549   What's your favorite place just to hang out?

1550   Do you believe in just giving kids an allowance or do you think they should earn it?

1551   Have you ever made your own orange juice?

1552   Have you ever been to a farmer's market, if so what do you love to get?

1553   If you had to give up one food you really love for the rest of your life, what would you pick?

1554   Would you rather have endless love or endless money?

1555   Name a famous person you wouldn't mind for a business partner.

1556   Do you have siblings, if not do you want some?

1557   What is your favorite name for a girl child?

1558   Are you a good judge of character?

1559   In a few short words describe what the word commitment means to you in dating.

1560   What is your favorite girls' name beginning with the letter E?

1561 Have you ever come to a crossroads in your life and what were the two paths?

1562 What three things do you think of most each day?

1563 Would you ever sign a prenuptial agreement?

1564 Would you travel to space if possible?

1565 What does creativity mean to you? Is it free flowing or does it involve your heart and soul?

1566 Where is one place you'd never be seen?

1567 What or who do you sympathize with?

1568 Would you feel any different if you suddenly found out you were adopted?

1569 What was the best present you received?

1570 If you were prime minister/ruler of the world what laws would you make?

1571 Have you ever been stood up for a date?

1572 Have you ever helped someone through a breakup and if so how did you help?

1573 Do you like ice in your drinks?

1574 How are your manners, do you say please and thank you?

1575 What is one of your favorite photos and what is the sentiment attached?

1576 How do you show hospitality when entertaining guests?

1577 What was your worst date ever?

1578 What is one good way to grab your attention?

1579 Do you believe in kissing on the first date?

1580 Have you ever gone back to a place that gave you horrible service, if so why?

1581 What crazy thing do you do when you think no one is looking?

1582 How many slices of pizza can you eat in one sitting?

1583 The quickest way to make you crazy is…

1584 Would you rather learn fencing or archery?

1585 What singer's voice gives you chills, in a good way?

1586 Have you ever made a ball of twine or rubber bands?

1587 Have you ever self-sabotaged, how?

1588 If you were going to become a doctor, what skill or trait would serve you well?

1589 Do you eat fast food, if so what's your favorite?

1590 At what age in your life did you learn the most?

1591   Do you goals and dreams energize you or exhaust you?

1592   Are you usually on time for things or are you habitually late?

1593   Do you have any hidden talents that would be considered strange?

1594   What's your favorite Saturday morning cartoon?

1595   Are you involved in your local community?

1596   Do you think it's more important to know CPR or self-defense?

1597   Have you ever witnessed a crime in progress, what kind of crime?

1598   Would you choose a shorter life and be super rich or a longer life somewhat poor?

1599   What instantly makes you not like another person?

1600   Someone you want to walk a mile in your shoes.

1601   Who is your ICE (in case of emergency) saved in your phone?

1602   If you could bring one famous person back from the dead, who would you pick?

1603   What celebrity man do you find ruggedly handsome?

1604   What do you think is the most dangerous profession in the whole world?

1605   What is something that always cheers you up?

1606   Does the term "settle down" scare you or give you comfort?

1607   Have you ever tried to get someone fired, if so why?

1608   How do you handle panhandlers?

1609   How tall is the tallest person you know?

1610   What is something you continuously procrastinate with?

1611   What's your favorite sport?

1612   What do you need more of?

1613   What upcoming life event are you excited about?

1614   What do you have a hard time visualizing?

1615   Do you prefer to live somewhere that has all four seasons of the weather?

1616   Do you think the grass is greener on the other side, or where you water it?

1617   What is one thing you'll never do in public?

1618   Do you think the Zombie Apocalypse could be real or is total make-believe?

1619   Are you scared of spiders?

1620   What dance or dance move have you mastered?

1621   Would you prefer to ride on a motorcycle or in a helicopter?

1622   Are you genuinely happy for other people's (family or friends) success?

1623   What is the best thing to happen to you this year?

1624   What memory from your school days still troubles you?

1625   If you could do one thing for someone and there were no limitations, what would it be?

1626   What's on your mind these days?

1627   What is your favorite thing to eat for breakfast that is not considered breakfast?

1628   What would you do differently if you knew nobody would judge you?

1629   How are you still similar to your younger self?

1630   What historical figure would you love to see in 21st century life?

1631   What or who brings your wild side to life?

1632   What is something that is possible today which 20 years ago would seem impossible?

1633   Do you give money to street performers?

1634   On a hot summer day what cools you off?

1635   What question are you always asked that offends or upsets you?

1636   If you were captain of a ship, what would you call it?

1637   What is a responsibility you have that you don't want?

1638   What is something you want people to remember about you?

1639   What is your vision for you and your family's future?

1640   Do you stay in your comfort zone most times or do you constantly push boundaries?

1641   What is your most used phrase?

1642   Do you allow yourself enough spare time to do things you love, if not why?

1643   Do you think secret clubs exist and if so what kind of club/s do you think there are?

1644   Do you think prisoners in jail should work so they can earn money for their release?

1645   What is the most unusual thing you've ever eaten?

1646   What actor or actress would you want to play you in a movie of your life?

1647   Are you the kind of friend you'd want as a friend?

1648   Have you ever tried archery?

1649   If you were a world famous art or jewel thief, what would be your next heist?

1650   What is something nice a neighbor has done for you?

1651   What gives you butterflies in your stomach?

1652   Who can you count on to tell you the truth when you need to hear it?

1653   What is something you fell in love with instantly, not a person?

1654   Have you ever used the yellow pages?

1655   Do you have any nervous habits?

1656   Who would win in a fight? Chuck Norris or Jack Bauer?

1657   Have you ever missed a good thing because you were focused on something else?

1658   Are you an over achiever or perfectionist?

1659   What does your "happy dance" look like?

1660   What makes you cry every time you think about it?

1661   Do you enjoy camping and if so where is your dream spot?

1662   Would you rather be the hero in a movie or the bad guy?

1663   How well do you handle yourself in formal settings?

1664   If you or your partner were pregnant, where would be the worst place to go into labor?

1665   Do you think they should continue to print books or go completely digital?

1666 What is your favorite love song?

1667 Do you think what a person tells a priest should be confidential, even if it's a crime?

1668 What is your favorite mythical creature beginning with the letter U?

1669 How many concerts have you attended in your life so far and which was the best?

1670 What do you feel should be mandatory for seriously wealthy people?

1671 What is one thing that doesn't add value to your life but you still do it?

1672 What still amazes you?

1673 What's something new you recently learned about yourself?

1674 What company or brand has the funniest commercials?

1675 Do you still listen to local stations on the radio or only streaming/playlist music?

1676 Could you tutor anyone in a subject?

1677 What moment from your life would make a good love song?

1678 What drains your energy really fast?

1679 What is a question you hate to ask?

1680 What 3 things will always happen in a typical day in your life?

1681   What was the most predictable moment of your life?

1682   What do you consider unforgivable?

1683   Have you ever attended an art opening or gallery opening, if so for who?

1684   What is the most bizarre thing you've ever Googled?

1685   What do you believe is the deadliest sin?

1686   Have you ever used money to influence anyone?

1687   What animal do you think is closest in intelligence to a human?

1688   Is there anything that you have told yourself is "off limits," if so what?

1689   What's the most thought provoking statement or question you've ever heard?

1690   Who makes you laugh without even trying?

1691   What do you think is the most harmful thing a person can do to their self?

1692   Are you easily offended?

1693   What is the most outside the box idea you ever had?

1694   Do you prefer to buy anything secondhand?

1695   What would you do with an extra hour in a day?

1696   What is something you love that is vintage?

1697   Name a fable that you can relate to?

1698   What news or media outlet do you trust?

1699   What was the last song you danced to?

1700   What is something people do you feel is the equivalent of playing Russian roulette?

1701   If you were a boss of many, would you want them to fear you or love you?

1702   Are you more of a homebody or a person about town?

1703   Do you like *Saturday Night Live* and if so who would you love to see as a new host?

1704   Your office or church is having a potluck dinner, what will you bring?

1705   Do you have money saved for a rainy day?

1706   What do you do when you feel the pressure of something is too much?

1707   What is the main thing you and your bestie have in common?

1708   What if any unusual objects have you swallowed?

1709   What do you think of *CNN?*

1710   If you could get away with murder, who would you kill?

1711   At this particular moment whom do you miss most right now?

1712   What would you compare your imagination to (one word)?

1713   What do you think would be one of the best steps we could take to end world poverty?

1714   Would you ever live in a treehouse?

1715   What makes you nervous?

1716   What wild animal scares you?

1717   Do you try to protect your reputation or does that not matter to you?

1718   What occasion do you pig out on food?

1719   On a scale of 1-10 how polite would you say you are?

1720   If you were comfortably rich would you work hard for more or rest on your laurels?

1721   Do you believe environmental surroundings play a role in future success?

1722   Would you ever start a celebrity fan club and if so for who?

1723   Have you ever had a "this can't be happening" moment and what was it?

1724   What faux pas do you find socially unacceptable?

1725   Where is the best place to meet new people if you're wanting to date?

1726 What is your favorite sport beginning with the letter S?

1727 How do you feel about buying a home?

1728 What TV show/s have you binge watched?

1729 Do you think most jurors can be impartial when presiding over a celebrity's trial?

1730 What's harder today than it was yesterday?

1731 What was your worst brain fart moment ever?

1732 What was your blessing in disguise?

1733 What keeps you interested in your goals or dreams?

1734 What do you consider to be irresponsible?

1735 If you achieved all your life's goals, how would you feel?

1736 What do you think is your greatest contribution to society?

1737 Do you think beauty pageants are degrading to women or harmless?

1738 What words do you always struggle to spell correctly?

1739 Would you rather be a news anchor, weather man/woman or an on location reporter?

1740 Have you ever taken a horse drawn carriage ride, and would you? Where?

1741   What was the topic of the worst argument you've ever had?

1742   Do you vote in every election?

1743   Do you think there is always something to be thankful for?

1744   How do you feel about the statement, "Home is where the heart is."

1745   What is one thing you thought existed but doesn't?

1746   What creative source or outlet do you often visit to get fresh ideas or renew your creativity?

1747   What do you need to learn to make time for?

1748   What are your bad habits?

1749   What's the biggest personal change you've ever made?

1750   What is your favorite animal beginning with the letter A?

1751   If you could star in any play you choose what character would you want to portray?

1752   Are you a left brainer or a right brainer?

1753   Something you want to forget.

1754   How many serious relationships have you had?

1755   If you were musically inclined whom would you want to have a private jam session with?

1756   Have you ever left words unspoken that you later regretted?

1757   What's the most thoughtful thing you've ever seen done for anyone or yourself?

1758   Is your dad an embarrassing dancer?

1759   Can you believe in something without evidence?

1760   What antiquated invention do you still use?

1761   How do you feel about guys wearing pink?

1762   What do consider yourself an expert at?

1763   What is the worst book you ever read?

1764   Do you like braided hair or dreadlocks?

1765   Did your childhood shape you into who you are today?

1766   What is your favorite thing about nature?

1767   Do you think you're living your life to the fullest?

1768   What is your solid foundation?

1769   What trap do you keep falling victim to?

1770   How are you at karaoke?

1771 Do you know the meaning of life?

1772 What would be your dream car?

1773 Have you ever had a roommate, if so what did you hate about it?

1774 Is there something you've tried to rectify but couldn't, if so what?

1778 Who do you feel is your kindred spirit?

1776 Do you appreciate and learn from criticism?

1777 Did you have a favorite teacher or a teacher who made a big impact on your life?

1778 Do you feel robbed in any area of your life, if so where and why do you feel this way?

1779 Where is your favorite place to get a massage?

1780 If the world had an apocalypse, could you hunt for your own food?

1781 What's your favorite thing to "add" to your soda or cola, cherries or something else?

1782 Do you think some people just want to be saved or rescued, why?

1783 Have you ever slept with a nightlight, if so do you still use it?

1784 What is your favorite item of clothing beginning with the letter B?

1785 Who and where was your most memorable kiss?

1786 What does your communication style say about you?

1787 What do you consider to be a feast?

1788 Do you still play with toys? If so what toy have you bought as an adult?

1789 If you had to bury treasure today, where would you hide it?

1790 Have you ever accidentally texted the wrong person and how did it turn out?

1791 What's your favorite pizza topping?

1792 What 3 musicians/singers do you feel contributed the most to music?

1793 If you could replace one body part with a bionic replacement which would you choose?

1794 Does any particular song play in your head when you walk?

1795 Do you like classical music, if so do you have a favorite composer?

1796 Are you a creature of habit, how?

1797 Have you ever been approached by someone familiar yet you couldn't remember them?

1798 Do you consider yourself above average, average or below average?

1799 What do you think would be the most boring job in the world for you?

1800 What was something you dreaded doing that you ended up loving?

1801 Do you snore?

1802 Have you or your parents been involved in any political rallies, events or protests?

1803 Have you ever built an igloo?

1804 How do you feel about people hunting big game animals like lions and elephants?

1808 What is best learning as you go?

1806 Do you currently have a blog, if so what's it about?

1807 Do you honor your commitments?

1808 What is your favorite parody?

1809 Have you ever had a pen pal and if so where did they live?

1810 What's the fanciest place you've ever dined at?

1811 What aroma or smell makes you feel alive?

1812 Do you see things in black and white or do you think there is a gray area in certain cases?

1813 Have you ever hurt someone on purpose, if so why?

1814 What good habits do you want to introduce into your daily routine?

1815 Do you subscribe to the mentality "if it sounds too good to be true, then it probably is?"

1816   Are you a planner or spontaneous?

1817   What is the biggest compromise you've made in your life?

1818   What technology advancement is overrated?

1819   Do you know any magic tricks?

1820   If you were going to take up painting as a hobby, what is the first thing you'd try to paint?

1821   Do you think artists should censor their work so they don't offend anyone?

1822   What is the first thing you notice about other people?

1823   What is the best thing about being your gender?

1824   What do you feel people complain too much about these days?

1825   What is the meanest prank you've pulled on someone or had pulled on you?

1826   If you swapped genders for a day how would you spend it?

1827   What's the most valuable thing you own?

1828   Have you ever built anything, if so what?

1829   Do you believe in spanking as a form of discipline or never?

1830   Who do you think is the best Olympian ever?

1831   What is one major political topic that you are undecided about?

1832   If you could instill one piece of advice in a baby's mind, what advice would you give?

1833   When you wake up in the morning what is your number 1 priority?

1834   Have you ever broken someone's heart?

1838   Do you eat after other people?

1836   There is Martin Luther King Jr. Day, etc. what historical figure should get a holiday?

1837   Why do you think bears hibernate?

1838   Do you prefer digital or rotary/analogue clocks?

1839   Does your family have a secret recipe and if so what's it for?

1840   What gives you chills every time?

1841   Beyond the titles that others have given you, who are you?

1842   What is your favorite luxury car or sports car?

1843   What is the rudest thing a person can do to another person in your opinion?

1844   What TV show really annoys you?

1845   What are most people afraid of that doesn't scare you?

1846   What's the main thing on your bucket list?

1847   Do you prefer a natural approach to healing or do you think modern drugs work best?

1848   What is the meaning of peace to you?

1849   Have you ever slipped on a banana peel?

1850   What type of contest do you think it would be fun to judge?

1851   What is your opinion of modern medicine?

1852   What do you think makes a good party host?

1853   In one word sum up society today.

1854   What do you do when you feel like you're stuck in rut?

1855   What drains your energy?

1856   If you had to design a playground for adults, what is one thing you'd put on it?

1857   If your significant other wanted to take a vacation without you, what would you say or do?

1858   Are you attracted to intelligence or does it matter?

1859   Would you ever eat something alive or gross for money?

1860   If you were the opposite sex for one day, what is one thing you'd do?

1861   What is taboo for you?

1862   If you could play God for a day, what's the first thing you'd do?

1863   What song would you say best sums you up?

1864   Who was better, The Beatles or Elvis Presley?

1868   When you make a decision do you stick to it or do you go back and forth?

1866   Do you feel where you're living now is the best fit for you?

1867   Which one of your friends do you think is the nicest?

1868   What is one way you've tried to conquer your fears?

1869   Where is the most magical place on earth in your opinion?

1870   Finish this sentence: If all else fails…

1871   Would you ever consider going back to school once you're over 50?

1872   What can someone learn from a baby boomer?

1873   Do you like stargazing?

1874   What do you take too seriously?

1875   Do you hold any special licenses or titles, if so which?

1876 Do you have any enemies?

1877 Do you think you have the capacity to learn how to fly a plane?

1878 What was the hardest change in your life you ever had to go through?

1879 Is there anything you wished would come back into fashion?

1880 If given your own show in Las Vegas what would you do?

1881 What specific thing makes you happy that would not make most people happy?

1882 How do you prefer your potatoes: baked, mashed, fries, scalloped, etc.?

1883 What do you feel connected to spiritually?

1884 What would the logo for your life look like?

1885 What do you do when you're stuck in traffic?

1886 Have you found the purpose of your life?

1887 What one trait do you have that will make you a great boss?

1888 Do you hoard anything, if so what?

1889 What is the cleverest phrase you know?

1890 Can you impersonate anyone famous?

1891   Have you ever stood up for anyone?

1892   What do you think is worse, failing or never trying?

1893   How high can you jump?

1894   What book have you read that made you really think about life?

1895   If they were going to name a street sign after you, what would you want the name to be?

1896   What's the most creative excuse to get out of doing something you didn't want to?

1897   If you became a writer what would you want to write?

1898   Do you wear sunglasses indoors to look cool or stylish?

1899   Which fictional married couple from TV or cartoons best fits your parents' marriage?

1900   What would you consider a challenge for yourself that may be rewarding in the long run?

1901   Have you ever stiffed a waiter/waitress for bad service or because you were being cheap?

1902   Do you think society puts too big an emphasis on physical appearance?

1903   Can you do 10 revolutions of a hula-hoop?

1904   Do you get sucked into the problems of your family, and how do you wiggle out of them?

1905   Can you make any animal's sounds, if so which one can you nail?

1906 What is one thing you've really wanted lately but haven't been able to get?

1907 What characteristics do you most respect in the opposite sex?

1908 Have you ever had to give someone devastating news, what was it about?

1909 Have you read anything by Agatha Christie, if so what book was your favorite?

1910 What is the most expensive thing you've ever lost?

1911 What is your favorite thing to do at the beach?

1912 If you were going to be invisible for a day, what would you do?

1913 What card game or game in general would you love to learn how to play?

1914 What is one of your favorite family traditions?

1915 How fast can you run?

1916 What seasonal food item do you love?

1917 Do you think after a certain age people should not be allowed to drive?

1918 If humans came with a warning label, what would yours say?

1919 What do you love most about summer?

1920 What do you consider is the most important appliance in a house?

1921   Do you prefer cats or dogs?

1922   What's your favorite aisle in the supermarket?

1923   Have you ever played *Apples to Apples,* if so what's the funniest answer you've heard?

1924   What is the most useless talent you have?

1925   Is there a new unreleased smartphone or electronic device you're excited to try?

1926   Do you think there will ever be a cure for cancer?

1927   Would you ever strike if you felt your employer wasn't treating you fairly?

1928   If you got into trouble and had to do community service, what would be the worst type?

1929   Do you play "brain games" that help exercise and strengthen your brain, if so what game?

1930   When was the last time you tried something new and what was it?

1931   Who can you be yourself around?

1932   Do you think parenting classes should be mandatory for all parents?

1933   What opinion do you have which would be very unpopular in the court of public opinion?

1934   If you were in the hospital who are the two people you'd want to be by your side?

1935   Would you ever consider writing to someone in jail as a pen pal?

1936 Do you have a festival or an event you look forward to each year that's not a holiday?

1937 Do you lick the yogurt or dessert lid?

1938 What movie director do you find completely disturbing?

1939 If you made a panic room, what would be some of the things found in there?

1940 Will you dye your hair if it starts turning gray?

1941 What is your favorite salty snack?

1942 Do you know how to ride a bike?

1943 Have you ever been in or had a food fight?

1944 Have you ever used someone and if so what for?

1945 Do you have a real life guardian angel, if so who is it?

1946 Have you ever been arrested, if so for what?

1947 Describe your sense of humor in one word.

1948 If you did ever have plastic surgery what procedure would you do?

1949 Have you ever had a prayer answered?

1950 Who has "society" deemed a hero that you feel isn't?

1951   What is your favorite brand of blue jeans?

1952   If your office had a show-n-tell for adults what thing would you be proud to display?

1953   What is your favorite type of casserole?

1954   What makes you keep your distance from someone or something?

1955   Do you watch any cooking shows, if so which ones?

1956   In what way are you too hard on yourself?

1957   If you wanted to live off the radar where would you live?

1958   If you could read one person's mind, who would it be?

1959   Can you do an impersonation of anyone?

1960   What was the most special handmade gift someone gave you?

1961   Did you ever have any pretend or imaginary friends?

1962   What are you a casual observer of?

1963   Do you correct people's mistakes?

1964   What technology are you excited about coming out?

1965   Have you ever reconsidered a major decision you've ever made, if so what?

1966 Did you play hide and seek as a kid, if so where was your best hiding place?

1967 Have you ever slapped someone?

1968 What is your favorite television station?

1969 What is a hobby you really want to try but worry you won't be good at?

1970 What is your favorite condiment?

1971 When did you last go to the beach?

1972 Have you ever been admitted to hospital?

1973 If you didn't want to serve jury duty, what's the most creative excuse you'd give?

1974 Do you have a "type" that you look for when dating a person?

1975 What is your favorite food beginning with the letter P?

1976 What's the most shocking moment of your life?

1977 What do you do when you're with someone and there is awkward silence?

1978 How old were you when you realized you had a gift and how did you express it?

1979 What TV show do you always watch re-runs of?

1980 If you could change one facial feature, what would it be?

1981   Do you believe in fairies?

1982   Your potential new boss says buy me a gift with the budget of $20.00. What will you buy?

1983   Who is the protagonist in your life?

1984   How are you your own worst enemy?

1985   What promise have you broken?

1986   Do you blame someone or something for the way your life is turning out?

1987   How do you feel about photography?

1988   If you lived in a tower would you want a doorman or do you think it's unnecessary, why?

1989   How many pairs of shoes do you own?

1990   What band do you find timeless?

1991   If you were a double agent, what would be your code name?

1992   What is the scariest movie you've ever seen?

1993   If you were famous who would you be excited to get interviewed by?

1994   What was the last thing to make you feel angry?

1995   What do people pick on you about?

1996 Have you ever rehearsed anything?

1997 If you were elected Mayor of your current city, what is the first thing you'd do?

1998 Does death scare you?

1999 Have you ever dieted, if so what diet did you try?

2000 If you had a year off of responsibilities, what would you want to do?

2001 When you're feeling sick, what makes you feel better?

2002 Have you ever gotten a warning about someone or something and ignored it, what was it?

2003 If you could have a themed birthday party, what would your theme be?

2004 What makes you stand out in a crowd?

2005 How did you meet the love of your life?

2006 What makes someone a good kisser in your opinion?

2007 What lesson to this day have you still not learned?

2008 What do you think is a good job for teenager just starting to learn responsibility?

2009 What's the oldest thing you own?

2010 What historical figure do you admire for devoting their life to doing good work?

2011 Do you own any inflatable furniture?

2012 What movie did you love but could only watch once?

2013 If you got lost in the woods what would you do?

2014 Do you excel in what you do currently?

2015 What do you think came first, the chicken or the egg?

2016 Could you ever be a living organ donor?

2017 Would you swim with sharks?

2018 What would be your perfect day?

2019 How do you feel about the kind of work you're doing right now?

2020 Do you like photography or videography better?

2021 What would you do if you saw someone getting bullied?

2022 Do you have a favorite number? Any particular reason why you like that number?

2023 What organization or cause would you volunteer for?

2024 What is your favorite trip down memory lane?

2025 What is one thing you'd never be caught wearing?

2026 What would be the moral of your story?

2027 What has been the biggest blindside in your life thus far?

2028 What does your style say about you?

2029 Which form of public transport do you prefer?

2030 Elementary through high school, what grade was the hardest for you?

2031 Do you always do the right thing?

2032 Do you think there will ever be a more sustainable substitute for gasoline? If so, what?

2033 Have you ever lost your faith in humanity, if so what caused it?

2034 If you were a geometric shape which would you be?

2035 What do you keep on your desk or workspace area that boosts your mood?

2036 What's in your perfect trail mix?

2037 What is one thing you think every human being should learn how to do?

2038 What non-profit organization would benefit from your skillset?

2039 What always puts a smile on your face?

2040 Do you prefer sunrises or sunsets?

2041   What do you think was the ugliest car model ever created?

2042   What would be the coolest design for a birthday cake?

2043   How do you feel about plastic surgery?

2044   What is the most outrageous question you've ever been asked by anyone?

2045   Do you think chivalry is dead...should it be?

2046   What food item do you no longer allow yourself to eat?

2047   What makes you feel unstoppable?

2048   Do you think it's better to be an only child or have siblings?

2049   How good are you at giving directions?

2050   What do you doubt more than anything?

2051   What is the craziest thing you'd do in a limo?

2052   What makes you proud?

2053   What are two funny traits about your mom you can describe?

2054   Have you ever won anything, if so what?

2055   Do you root for the underdogs, if so who is your favorite underdog from literature?

2056 If you lost everything you worked for tomorrow, what's the first step in starting over?

2057 Something you believe in that others think is not real.

2058 What social media platform are you most active on?

2059 What's the simplest way you have fun?

2060 Do you think two people that don't speak the same language could be in a relationship?

2061 Does the sight of blood make you queasy?

2062 What is a promise you know you'll never break?

2063 Do you think you need to slow down and enjoy life more?

2064 How do you cope with loss or death?

2065 What book from your childhood book would you want to read to your children?

2066 What moment from your life would you love to live over and over?

2067 What news story are you tired of hearing about?

2068 How did you meet your significant other (if single, your last one)?

2069 Who made the worst first impression on you but then later became your friend?

2070 Have you ever slept outdoors?

2071   Would you rather be hated or forgotten?

2072   How do you handle negative influences in your life?

2073   If you were going to speak to a group of graduating teenagers, what would be the topic?

2074   What insulting term or word do people use very cavalier today?

2075   What is your favorite personality trait you like about yourself?

2076   Have you ever been caught in a compromising position? Even despite a valid explanation?

2077   Do you know how to use a compass, and how well?

2078   Do you like hot or cold food better?

2079   Do you jog or walk regularly, if so where is your favorite place to go for a run?

2080   Do you know how to use any weapons, if so which ones?

2081   What is your favorite movie quote?

2082   Do you think science is cool or creepy?

2083   When you look into the mirror, what's the first word that comes to mind?

2084   How did your parents meet?

2085   What is the most beneficial Chinese proverb?

2086   Who is the one person you hug that you don't want to let go?

2087   When you were in grade school did you bring your lunch or buy it from the school?

2088   In a disagreement, do you think it's better to be right or peaceful?

2089   Is it better to give than receive in your opinion or are you the opposite?

2090   Do you have a lawyer?

2091   Are you the kind of person to step in and try to break up a fight?

2092   If you had to take a couples class, what kind of class would be fun to take with your boo?

2093   What's the tallest building you've ever been up?

2094   What is one thing you wish you knew about your grandparents?

2095   What is your "go-to" comfort food?

2096   Worst thing you've eaten at a dinner party?

2097   Do you think money is the root of all evil?

2098   What do you hope for?

2099   Who do you hope to forge a relationship with business or otherwise in the future?

2100   What's the most unusual conversation you've ever had?

2101 Can you do any fake accents, if so which one?

2102 What home design trend do you love?

2103 What do you feel very protective of?

2104 Have you ever loved two people at one time and were conflicted about whom to choose?

2105 What do you compartmentalize in your life?

2106 What is your most favorite random fact?

2107 Who is the strangest person you've ever met?

2108 Are you a drama king or queen?

2109 Have you ever been in a fight?

2110 What do you dislike most about the current city you live in?

2111 Do you let your conscience guide you?

2112 Have you ever wielded a sword?

2113 When have you answered someone's cry for help?

2114 Do you often help people when they ask or does there have to be something in it for you?

2115 What is the most unusual name you've ever heard of?

2116 Do you think you could write a song, if so what would it be about?

2117 Do you put up a boundary on any area of your life to keep people out?

2118 If you had a chance to marry royalty would you, even if you weren't in love?

2119 Who do you feel like you have the strongest unspoken bond with?

2120 Have you ever blackmailed someone, if so with what?

2121 What is some of the most important work being researched on our planet in your opinion?

2122 Have you ever won a giant sized toy from a fair?

2123 Have you ever been caught in a love triangle, if so with who?

2124 Do you know the valedictorian of your high school class and where are they now?

2125 What is your most used word?

2126 Do you prefer flowers or plants or both?

2127 Do you like cheese, if so what is your favorite kind?

2128 Do you think there should be special laws for the paparazzi?

2129 Are you introverted or extroverted?

2130 Do you think some people in certain situations might be more valuable than others?

2131   What is the trait you most deplore in others?

2132   What brings out your silly side?

2133   Do you trust things you read online, if so what is your most reliable source?

2134   Do you do what you say you're going to do?

2135   What would you hire a private detective for?

2136   What is childish but you still do it anyway?

2137   What is one thing you'd recommend people not try or do?

2138   Whom do you secretly envy?

2139   If you found a purse with $100 on the floor, would you turn it in?

2140   Do you have a favorite figurine or action figure, if so who is it of?

2141   Do you buy recycled products and goods and how do you feel about it?

2142   What villain from history do you think was misunderstood?

2143   Have you ever gone on a sightseeing tour, if so where?

2144   If you could have fame but not control of your career, would you still want to be famous?

2145   Would you rather have a cool boss and learn nothing or a strict boss you learn from?

2146 Do you have a hard time telling people no?

2147 Would you ever consider becoming a preacher?

2148 What do you do when you get really angry?

2149 If you could do something all over again, what would it be?

2150 Have you ever received or bought a gag gift, if so what was it?

2151 Life is too short so you need to stop and...

2152 What is one thing you will never give up on?

2153 What is your favorite gum?

2154 What table manner do people lack that drives you crazy?

2155 Do you need to learn how to say NO more often?

2156 What do you think every couple should do on their honeymoon?

2157 Was there something you asked for repeatedly as a child, that you were always told no?

2158 Do you think a person can always depend on the kindness of strangers?

2159 Have you ever thrown a temper tantrum until you got your way?

2160 Which do you think is worse, airplane food or hospital food?

2161 What strokes your ego?

2162 How sophisticated are you?

2163 If you live to be 100 years old, will you want to do something extra special?

2164 What kind of driver are you?

2165 What is your biggest turnoff?

2166 When you lose touch, what snaps you back to reality?

2167 If you could afford a personal driver to drive you everywhere, would you get one?

2168 Who do you think has done the most for human rights throughout history?

2169 What is one thing you'd never do for all the money in the world?

2170 Could you marry someone with different political beliefs than your own?

2171 What is the greatest peer pressure you've ever felt?

2172 Have you ever been a part of a team and how'd that make you feel?

2173 Have you ever done a criminal background check on someone you've dated?

2174 What should kids be sheltered from, if anything?

2175 How long could you go without talking?

2176 What are you worried will change you?

2177 What triggers your inner shopaholic?

2178 Do you have a scar, if so how did you get it?

2179 What part of democracy do you not agree with?

2180 How cynical are you?

2181 If you need to come up with a large amount of money in 48 hours, how could you do it?

2182 What do you feel needs further exploration in our world or universe?

2183 Who is the smartest person you know and what do you ask them for help with?

2184 What is the hardest thing about being YOU?

2185 How tall are you?

2186 How would you rate your athleticism using fictional characters?

2187 Have you ever given a speech, if so what about?

2188 Have you ever declared a truce with someone you were fighting with?

2189 Have you ever run into a wall or door?

2190 Do you think happiness is a choice?

2191   How would you describe your sarcasm?

2192   Do you like to meet new people?

2193   What new TV show recently released do you love?

2194   Why did you choose your current profession?

2195   What's your favorite holiday time cartoon?

2196   Are you conservative, liberal or somewhere in between?

2197   If you were given $1,000 to spend on your closest friend, what would you get them?

2198   Have you ever gotten in a bidding war on Ebay, if so for what item?

2199   Can you do any tricks with your tongue?

2200   What is a recent compliment you've received?

2201   Who is your favorite radio DJ?

2202   Do you think a little competition is healthy?

2203   What is the ultimate cake topping?

2204   Where is heaven on earth in your opinion?

2205   Can you juggle?

2206   Do you believe in heaven and hell?

2207   What has been your worst haircut/style?

2208   What were you doing exactly a year ago that's different than today?

2209   Is there a family member who you don't associate with anymore, and why?

2210   What do you think is the most beautiful word?

2211   Have you ever ridden on a motorcycle, would you?

2212   Are you friends with any of your ex's?

2213   Who would you want to be stranded on an island with?

2214   What are you good at guessing?

2215   What does "The American Dream" mean to you?

2216   Have you ever had a brush with insanity, how?

2217   If you wrote an excerpt about the craziest day of your life would it read as fact or fiction?

2218   Have you ever been a bartender, would you?

2219   What is the last thing someone talked you into doing that you didn't want to do?

2220   Which foreign language did you have to learn at school?

2221 What do you think the female version of James Bond should be called?

2222 What should we take measure of that we currently don't?

2223 What would you do if you found out you had a sibling you'd never met?

2224 Have you ever caused a scene, if so where?

2225 Have you ever participated in "flash mob" if so what song and dance did you do?

2226 If you could learn any language fluently what would it be?

2227 Would you rather explore a new planet, or the depths of the ocean?

2228 How do you like your eggs?

2229 Do you think unicorns ever existed, prehistorically or otherwise?

2230 What is special about your hometown?

2231 Have you ever had a secret admirer?

2232 What is the strangest thing someone might find under your bed?

2233 Have you ever gotten stuck anywhere and if so where?

2234 When was the last time you listened to the sound of your own breathing?

2235 Do you have a reoccurring New Year's resolution?

2236 What is your favorite song to sing in the shower or while you drive?

2237 Do you think people should learn to limit their cell phone use?

2238 Out of all the dreams you've had for your life, what was your biggest dream of all?

2239 What should be banned in your country that currently isn't?

2240 Are you scared of the dark?

2241 If you could make a fictional character or cartoon come to life, who would you choose?

2242 What are 3 things you look for in a partner?

2243 Have you ever licked the spoon and if so what is your favorite thing to lick?

2244 If you and a friend both wanted the same thing would you let the friend have it first?

2245 What metaphor best describes your life?

2246 What is one thing you really want to change about your appearance?

2247 Have you ever been served breakfast in bed, if yes by who and why?

2248 What is your favorite book beginning with the letter F?

2249 Have you ever prank called someone and if so what did you say?

2250 What is one life story you plan on telling your grandchildren about?

2251 If your 5 year old self were looking at you today, would it recognize you?

2252 Who is the one person you'd love to have as a mentor?

2253 What is one thing you always get when you go to the store?

2254 Do you get seasick?

2255 Have you ever gotten sick from eating too much?

2256 What is your favorite thing to put in the freezer to eat or drink that normally isn't?

2257 If you started training for the Olympics, what event would you have a realistic chance at?

2258 If you were going to join a music band past or present, what band would you fit in best?

2259 How long do you think you could last without your smartphone or internet?

2260 Is someone's word enough for you or do you need more?

2261 What is your favorite eye color on someone else, why?

2262 Does anything make you feel claustrophobic?

2263 What do you have on your fridge door?

2264 What is the most unusual thing you've done on a date?

2265 Have you ever been laid off from a job?

2266 Do you sleep on your back, stomach, or side?

2267 What is your favorite magazine cover of all-time?

2268 What is your favorite conversation topic?

2269 What is the biggest favor someone has asked you for?

2270 What do you have now as an adult that you really wanted as a kid?

2271 Do you like cake or pie more?

2272 Have you ever met anyone infamous, who?

2273 Have you ever quit your job, if so why?

2274 What keeps you up at night?

2275 If you were designing a haunted house, what is the main scary thing you would have?

2276 Have you ever sold anything online, if so where and why?

2277 Do you agree with the statement "love never fails"?

2278 Your favorite cologne or perfume?

2279 How many times have you fallen in love?

2280 Do you think people with freckles are attractive?

2281 When was the last time you were really stumped and what stumped you?

2282 What decade would you love to have grown up in?

2283 Are you a good singer?

2284 Have you ever not gotten involved in something where you should have, what was it?

2285 Have you ever gone to a psychic?

2286 What is your proudest accomplishment?

2287 Have you ever walked into a wall?

2288 Do you apologize when you're wrong?

2289 If you could wipe one thing off the planet who or what would it be?

2290 Who's your favorite mythological figure from ancient history?

2291 Where do you like to go to on a first date?

2292 Do you go with the flow or against the grain?

2293 What did you want to be when you were growing up?

2294 Do you make rash judgements of people too often?

2295 What do you think your life represents?

2296   If you could go back in time to change one thing what would it be?

2297   What do you miss the most often in your life?

2298   Do you think crying is a sign of weakness or strength?

2299   What celebrity has the best narrator's voice?

2300   If you could change your eye color what would it be?

2301   What is your favorite movie genre?

2302   What hate or hatred have you held onto?

2303   What is your spirit animal?

2304   Have you ever baked your own cake?

2305   Do you have a specific brand of bottled water you like or do you think water is water?

2306   Are you strategic, if so how many steps ahead do you think?

2307   Do you have a sweet tooth or a savory tooth?

2308   What brings out your "beast mode"?

2309   Have you read any self-help books and has any book in particular stood out?

2310   Is there something most people consider a bad habit that you disagree with?

2311   Do you think you could be a single parent and raise a child alone?

2312   What was your favorite subject in school?

2313   What makes a physically attractive person less attractive?

2314   What was the last movie you rented?

2315   Describe a time in your life when the phrase "when it rains, it pours" applied.

2316   Have you ever not returned something you borrowed and if so what was it?

2317   Have you ever been someone's secret admirer and if so what did you send them?

2318   What website do you visit the most?

2319   Do you prefer vertical or horizontal stripes?

2320   How scared of the dark are you?

2321   What are you biased about?

2322   What healthy lifestyle change have you made?

2323   What is your favorite poem?

2324   What do you think is the most fundamental value to keep intact?

2325   What's the best museum you've ever been to?

2326 If you had to rate yourself on a scale of 1-10, what would you rate yourself?

2327 What do you like better falling in love or actually being in love?

2328 Do you think you're a good person?

2329 What is your favorite game to play with multiple people?

2330 Have you ever played the bongos?

2331 Do you think diseases and length of age are genetics or does health and exercise matter?

2332 When you were a kid what did your family usually do together?

2333 What did you love about your neighborhood growing up?

2334 Have you ever dedicated a song to anyone, what song?

2335 Do you think sophistication is overrated or undervalued in today's society?

2336 Other than money, what do you want to be prosperous in?

2337 Would you ever take dance lessons and what dance in particular would you want to learn?

2338 If you could ring in a New Year anywhere in the world, where would you choose?

2339 What should be the biggest global worry about the future?

2340 Where did you meet your closest friend?

2341   What are you generous with?

2342   If you were to write a song, what would it be about?

2343   Do you like to read or write more, or both equally?

2344   Did you join a fraternity or sorority? Would you? Why or why not?

2345   What would you like to achieve through your work?

2346   Did you ever have a teacher you felt was unfair to you, if so how?

2347   If you were going to become a doctor, what would be your field of specialty?

2348   What was your favorite thing to do after school as a kid?

2349   Pretend you're doing an interview, who would you pick and what's the first question?

2350   What do you appreciate?

2351   If there werc a real vigilante killing bad criminals, would you want them to be punished?

2352   What do you worry about too much?

2353   What was your funniest computer or phone wallpaper?

2354   Do you always calculate risk or are some rewards worth throwing caution to the wind?

2355   Where could you take more of a leadership role?

2356   What is your favorite fruit?

2357   Do you stand in solidarity with any cause or anyone?

2358   Do you believe in turning the other cheek?

2359   Have you ever accidentally injured anyone?

2360   If you knew your best friend's significant other was lying, would you tell them?

2361   All roads lead to what...?

2362   If you could pick one gadget from any superhero to own, what would it be?

2363   What is the highest speed you've ever driven in a car, how did it make you feel?

2364   What do you give yourself permission to do that is nobody else's business?

2365   What wisdom do you like to share?

2366   Did you ever compete in a science fair and if so what did you make?

2367   What is a place you think everyone should visit?

2368   If you have a child, what is one thing you'd never let them do?

2369   Do you have a funny nickname for something other than yourself?

2370   Do you shop on Black Friday for deals, if so what's the best deal you ever got?

2371   What feels spiritual to you?

2372   Have you ever had an out of body experience, if so describe it in one word?

2373   When was the last time you cried and what made you cry?

2374   What is your worst vacation memory?

2375   If your friends need you, are you there for them?

2376   What is the most interesting thing you've researched?

2377   How much attention do you require?

2378   What are the biggest drawbacks of your current job?

2379   What's your outlook on life?

2380   When you were a kid did you have a favourite amusement park ride?

2381   When you were young did you ever sneak out after curfew, if so where did you go?

2382   Are you a good artist?

2383   Have you ever had surgery and if so what for?

2384   Have you ever been hospitalized, if so why?

2385   Are you a workaholic?

2386 Do you have any old friends you wish you could meet up with again?

2387 If you joined a rock band what position would you want?

2388 Do you know your own worth?

2389 If you were designing your own fragrance to represent you, what would you call it?

2390 What did you do for your 21st birthday, if you're not 21 what are you planning for it?

2391 What is something that gave you buyer's remorse?

2392 Do you know how to jump rope?

2393 When it's your birthday do you always wear a birthday hat?

2394 What present do you think is appropriate to give a teacher in appreciation?

2395 What is your favorite ride at any amusement park?

2396 Describe your most independent decision or moment without others' influence?

2397 Have you ever made a scrapbook for yourself or someone else, what was in it?

2398 Do you do anything "part-time"?

2399 In a relationship do you believe in joint or separate bank accounts?

2400 Do you think friends make better lovers or that friends should never cross that line?

2401   How would you feel making someone else's dream come true?

2402   Where is your home away from home?

2403   What health topic have you done tons of research on to better your life?

2404   What specific act or contribution have you done for the environment?

2405   If you got arrested, who is the first person you'd call?

2406   Has anyone started a rumor about you, if so what was it about?

2407   You're starting a band in the morning, what's your band's name?

2408   Pick a board game that describes your love life?

2409   Have you ever been to Legoland?

2410   What is your favorite sandwich?

2411   At what age did you catch on to the fact that Santa wasn't real?

2412   Do you think Bigfoot is real?

2413   Do you think a full moon can have an effect on a person?

2414   Could you work in a morgue if the pay was really good, and why?

2415   What reality TV show do you think it would be fun to appear on?

2416   How popular were you in school?

2417   Have you ever followed an infamous criminal case broadcasting and if so what case?

2418   What one thing do you know to be true?

2419   Do you decorate your home for the holidays, if so how?

2420   Have you ever raised money for charity?

2421   Compare yourself to the metamorphosis of something.

2422   What do you love about winter?

2423   Did you ever have a babysitter and if so what is one thing you remember about them?

2424   What actor or actress is not valued or appreciated enough?

2425   What is a big obstacle or harmful for new marriages today?

2426   Have you ever bought anything from an infomercial, if so what?

2427   Do you feel younger or older than your actual age?

2428   What life lesson was hardest to learn?

2429   What 3 things are on your dream home wish list?

2430   Is there a new hobby you want to try? What is it?

2431   How fast can you get changed?

2432   In your opinion, what is the worst invention ever?

2433   What's the most embarrassing thing your father has ever said to you?

2434   How self-aware are you?

2435   What song do you know ALL the words to?

2436   What was the worst present you received?

2437   Do people often ask you for your opinion and do you give it freely?

2438   Do you have a list of things to do before you're "x" years old?

2439   What is something you're really good at but hate doing?

2440   What is your "go-to" accessory?

2441   Do you collect anything?

2442   Do you appreciate constructive criticism?

2443   What conspiracy do you think has merit or is real?

2444   What card game are you awesome at?

2445   What is your favorite name for a boy child?

2446   What creative gift do you know for sure you have?

2447   What is something people should know about you?

2448   What do you owe yourself?

2449   What piques your curiosity?

2450   Have you ever been dumped?

2451   Have you ever given a present to someone that they hated/disliked?

2452   Do you pick out all your outfits for the week or just decide in the morning?

2453   Do you believe in perfection?

2454   Are you usually "the life of the party"?

2455   Do you believe in capital punishment?

2456   Who makes your favorite pair of shoes?

2457   What was a specific turning point in your life?

2458   On a scale of 1-10 how funny would you say you are?

2459   Do you love or hate rollercoasters?

2460   Have you ever bent the rules to get ahead?

2461 What kind of product could you never volunteer to be a taste tester for?

2462 What's the most embarrassing or worst thing your parents ever caught you doing?

2463 When you pack your lunch for work or school, what is your favorite packed lunch?

2464 Have you ever ridden a tractor?

2465 If you discover a new species what would you name it?

2466 Are you scared of thunderstorms?

2467 Have you ever been banned from a public place?

2468 If you could choose the profession of your child would you or would you let them choose?

2469 What fairy tale character do you most relate to?

2470 In the event of a divorce who do you think should decide where the child lives?

2471 Have you ever felt ashamed of anyone or anything?

2472 In your opinion who was the worst dictator in all of history?

2473 What new memories do you want to make?

2474 What is the largest amount of money you've had to borrow off someone?

2475 What is your favorite animated or cartoon program?

2476 Have you ever eavesdropped on someone, and if so what did you hear?

2477 Where do you see yourself in 10 years' time?

2478 Where is your favorite place to window shop?

2479 Other than candy, what do you think is a good trick or treat to hand out on Halloween?

2480 What is your favorite type of seafood?

2481 Would you join in a revolution?

2482 Do you count your chickens before they hatch, if so how?

2483 If you could breed two species together what new animal would you create?

2484 Are you scared of needles?

2485 As a society what could we all do better?

2486 Where did you watch your most memorable sunset?

2487 When was the last time you lost your temper? About what?

2488 Do you think babies are little bundles of joy or smelly noisy things?

2489 Have you ever gone out in public in your pajamas, where did you go?

2490 Would you accept a fatal mission in exchange for lifetime of support for your family?

2491   What was your first car (or what would you like it to be)?

2492   Do you consider your pet a part of your family or like your child?

2493   Have you ever met any celebrities?

2494   If you could change your name, what new name would you want?

2495   Are you a better friend to your friends than they are to you?

2496   What anagram can be formed from your name?

2497   Do you believe the truth will set you free or is it overrated?

2498   If you won a million dollars but had to give it all away in 24 hours, how would you do it?

2499   Do you make a pro and con list or just go with your gut?

2500   What superstition are you most afraid will give you bad luck for real?

2501   What do you like to do at the park?

2502   Would you rather be a worried genius or a joyful simpleton?

2503   Have you ever had a long distance relationship?

2504   If you could have an extra hour in the day, what would you do with it?

2505   What is a subject in school you hated?

2506   What was the worst case of mistaken identity you're aware of?

2507   Have you ever had chicken pox?

2508   Do you think morals are universal or relative?

2509   How well do you stand your ground?

2510   What's the most fun card game?

2511   If you became powerful do you worry you'd abuse your power?

2512   What is one thing you love about the country you were born in?

2513   Are you all talk, all action or a little of both?

2514   What have you lost touch with?

2515   Have you ever test driven a car you knew you weren't going to buy, if so what?

2516   Did you ever wear glasses, braces or something different—how did it make you feel?

2517   Would you steal to feed a starving child?

2518   How do you cheer up someone having a bad day?

2519   What is one thing you hate about the holiday season?

2520   In your opinion what's the one thing someone getting married should do for their big day?

2521 How far up Mt. Everest do you think you'd get if you had to climb it tomorrow?

2522 What do you typically have for breakfast?

2523 What carb are you addicted to?

2524 What age did you hit puberty and what was the worst thing about it?

2525 What is really complicated about your life?

2526 If you could afford to hire a personal assistant, what tasks would you give them to do?

2527 Have you ever been to an art gallery?

2528 What's the silliest thing you've ever cried about?

2529 How frugal are you?

2530 What gets better with age?

2531 How important is starting and having a family to you?

2532 Do you think the description of life as a roller coaster is accurate or not?

2533 What matters most to you?

2534 Do you know any identical twins?

2535 What's the worst movie you ever saw in a movie theater?

2536   Are you old-fashioned?

2537   What position do you often sleep in?

2538   What is the most daring thing you've done?

2539   Who do you think is the greatest sports athlete ever?

2540   Would you live in a castle?

2541   Have you ever remained friends with an ex-lover?

2542   What things do you want to have in common with your significant other?

2543   Are you pretty devious?

2544   What is your favorite thing to do in front of a fireplace?

2545   What is something gross you've done, that you'd die of shame if anyone found out?

2546   Do you believe in love at first sight?

2547   Are all men and women created equal?

2548   Who is a male role model in your life?

2549   What is the greatest crime against humanity?

2550   Who is the legend of all legends in your opinion?

2551   If you were a super hero what outfit would you wear?

2552   What's your favorite cereal?

2553   How do you flirt with someone?

2554   Who is your favorite comedian?

2555   How would you describe yourself to a blind person in 5 words or less?

2556   Do you like dressing up or do you prefer to always keep it casual?

2557   If you were going on a road trip what are the 3 "must-haves" you couldn't leave without?

2558   Can you honestly say you're enjoying your life right now?

2559   If you're having a bad day, what makes it better?

2560   How often do you lie?

2561   Do you suck or bite lollipops?

2562   What are three things you can't live without?

2563   If you were married and you had trouble in your relationship, would you go to counseling?

2564   Have you ever been a member of a club?

2565   Have you ever exacted revenge on someone, what did they do to you?

2566   What is your most valuable skillset?

2567   Have you ever been in a helicopter?

2568   Who was the best boss you ever had and what made them the best?

2569   What is currently taxed that you feel should have no taxes?

2570   Do you know any self defense moves or martial arts?

2571   What do you find cliché?

2572   Who is your favorite crooner?

2573   What makes a person trustworthy in your opinion?

2574   What is your favorite style of architecture?

2575   What actor or actress would play you in a documentary?

2576   When you're looking to meet someone with relationship potential, where is the best place?

2577   What song best describes your life?

2578   If you were making a care package for your enemy what would you put in it?

2579   Do you ever make your own greeting cards?

2580   What are you still looking forward to most in your life?

2581   Do you like to always look your best?

2582   For a romantic picnic what are the 2 most important things?

2583   What is your favorite music video of all time?

2584   What helps you keep things in perspective?

2585   The world is flooding and you must build a small ark, which 7 animals would you save?

2586   What gives you pause?

2587   What is the worst dare you've ever been given and did you do it?

2588   Do you respect authority?

2589   Do you like musicals?

2590   Have you ever settled for something?

2591   Which living person do you most admire?

2592   Do you get over-involved with TV or movie plots?

2593   Do you think marriage is still sacred in today's society?

2594   If you could wave a magic wand and make something happen right now, what would it be?

2595   Have you ever thrown a pity party for yourself and if so what about?

2596   What do you typically drink with your meals?

2597   You're creating an entirely new kind of potato chip, what flavor is it?

2598   What culture or lifestyle different than yours would you love to live in and explore?

2599   If you could sing a duet with anyone, who would it be?

2600   What would be the funniest thing you'd say to a cop to get out of a ticket?

2601   What caused the worst injury you ever had?

2602   Have you ever been hazed, if so how?

2603   What instantly pushes your buttons?

2604   What movie do you wish life was more like?

2605   Who are you trying too hard to please?

2606   Can you blow a bubble with bubblegum?

2607   Have you ever gotten insomnia and if so what gives it to you?

2608   Who was the last person you said "I love you" to?

2609   What makes you feel uncomfortable in group settings?

2610   Are you saving for retirement or do you think you still have time?

2611   If you were a giant mega monster what city would you rampage?

2612   Have you ever performed in front of a large audience?

2613   Have you ever contested anything?

2614   Are you a hypochondriac or the opposite?

2615   What color combination do you love together?

2616   How do you take care of your emotional well-being?

2617   Is there someone that you truly hate?

2618   Have you and your best friend ever been interested in the same person?

2619   What scared you as a child?

2620   What superhero would you love to date (if you were single)?

2621   Do you trust the police?

2622   Is torture ever a good option? If no, why not? If yes, when?

2623   What would you do if you won the lottery?

2624   Where are you ticklish?

2625   Has anyone given you a gift that was inscribed, if so what did it say?

2626 What's a belief that you hold with which many people disagree?

2627 Do you think it's tacky or romantic to elope and get married in Las Vegas?

2628 What is one thing you wish you'd spent more time doing when you were younger?

2629 Is there a food you hated as a kid but now love as an adult?

2630 What is your favorite actor beginning with the letter K?

2631 Do you still spend pennies, what do you do with them?

2632 Do you live by any special philosophy?

2633 Jason Bourne or James Bond–who is your favorite spy?

2634 Have you ever been rejected by anyone?

2635 What personality trait gets you into trouble?

2636 What is something you don't mind sharing with other people?

2637 Do you buy any weekly/monthly magazines?

2638 How do you settle your nerves?

2639 What is the worst grudge you ever held?

2640 Would you rather learn sign language or a foreign language of your choice?

2641 Do you think the 2016 U.S. Presidential outcome will affect you?

2642 What was your sink or swim moment?

2643 What are you never satisfied with?

2644 Do you think paper money will eventually be replaced and if so by what?

2645 What do you dread?

2646 How much do you trust doctors?

2647 Do you make wishes when you blow out your birthday candles, and have any come true?

2648 Do you have much of an ego?

2649 Have you ever milked a cow and if not would you try?

2650 Do you and your significant other have a special song, if so what is it?

2651 What answers are you searching for?

2652 Have you ever re-gifted a present you received and if so what was it?

2653 Do you believe the government hides technology and information from the public?

2654 What helps you gain insight?

2655 What is your secret to success?

2656   What's the strangest thing you've ever seen in the middle of the road?

2657   What have you decided to dedicate your life to doing?

2658   What is the strangest skeleton you ever discovered in someone's closet?

2659   Did you ever lose respect for someone you once really respected, who?

2660   Have you ever had a crisis of faith, if so what triggered it?

2661   If you were to join one of the armed forces which would it be?

2662   What is your favorite kind of pet?

2663   Have you ever seen a shooting star, meteor shower or any other astronomical event?

2664   Who do you sometimes compare yourself to?

2665   What is the funniest punchline to a joke you've ever heard?

2666   Your favorite thing to do when couch surfing?

2667   How do you feel about global warming (use one sentence)?

2668   What good habits have you recently developed?

2669   What is something your parents love that you actually love too?

2670   What Disney character do you love the most?

2671 What's your favorite flavor of salad dressing?

2672 When you close your eyes what do you see?

2673 Would there ever be a reason you'd support war?

2674 Have you ever accidentally set fire to yourself?

2675 Who do you like to shop with?

2676 Where do you go when you need to blow off some steam?

2677 Do you think you can learn something from everyone you meet?

2678 What historic person would you love as a mentor?

2679 How much money a year do you spend on clothing?

2680 What is a bigger fear for you: getting a shot from the doctor or going to the dentist?

2681 Are you the kind of friend you'd want to have as a friend yourself?

2682 What beach do you want to visit?

2683 Do you think companies should be able to use lie detector tests for work incidences?

2684 Back in high school what was the strangest thing someone could find in your locker?

2685 What is your favorite precious metal?

2686   What is the one thing you always got away with as a kid?

2687   What holiday do you think is nonsense?

2688   What was something you learned in school that is absolutely useless in life?

2689   What's the worst thing about your life?

2690   Have you ever had a "false alarm" moment, what was it about?

2691   Do you prefer baths or showers?

2692   What is your birthstone?

2693   Do you think whaling should be allowed?

2694   What was the first car you ever owned?

2695   Have you ever been to a rodeo?

2696   Have you ever participated in a focus group, if so for what?

2697   Do you think taking naps is a good thing or healthy?

2698   What makes you original?

2699   Do you think Valentine's Day is romantic or just too commercial?

2700   If you were told you had to downsize your life, where's the first place you'd start?

2701   What is your favorite country beginning with the letter Z?

2702   If the world was ending tomorrow, what would you do today?

2703   Do you consider yourself a DIY person?

2704   What is the best thing you bring into a friendship?

2705   If you could make one of your hobbies into a profession, which one would it be?

2706   What did you do on your most memorable summer vacation away from school?

2707   If you could be President of the U.S. for a day, what would be your first order of business?

2708   What is your perfect birthday cake?

2709   What small act of kindness were you once shown that you will never forget?

2710   What is your all-time favorite sports team?

2711   What is your biggest motivation?

2712   What phrase or quote best describes you?

2713   What's the longest you've gone without sleep?

2714   Do you give up easily or are you a fighter?

2715   Does your name have a special or significant meaning, if so what?

2716 Who is the most famous person you've ever met?

2717 What is something from your childhood that you still have to this day?

2718 Have you ever sold your services?

2719 What do you love most about where you live now?

2720 What social issue weighs on your mind?

2721 What question should you never ask someone you just met?

2722 What is a lie your parents or teachers would always tell you?

2723 What is your zodiac sign and do the behavior traits fit your personality?

2724 Is the glass half empty or half full?

2725 Have you ever argued over who should pay for something?

2726 Is there something you need to tell your family but are afraid to?

2727 What movement in history helped shape your life?

2728 What is one thing a role model should always do in your opinion?

2729 What is a vice you won't part with?

2730 Do you think there is a real Loch Ness Monster?

2731　Who or what motivates you?

2732　Do you consider yourself a team player?

2733　If you got to nominate the next President of the U.S., who would get your endorsement?

2734　What or who do you have an unhealthy relationship with?

2735　Do you have a favorite podcast?

2736　What is one thing you can do today you could not do a year ago?

2737　Do you think it's a thin line between love and hate?

2738　If you could change one thing about the U.S. Constitution what would it be?

2739　What is the scariest ghost story you've ever heard?

2740　What is something you're afraid to try?

2741　What's your favorite day of the week?

2742　Do you have anything autographed by a celebrity?

2743　What age would you like to retire?

2744　Who is one person from history who was taken too soon?

2745　Is there anything standing in the way of your happiness?

2746   What is your favorite Christmas or holiday tradition?

2747   Do you have a signature move or quirk that people notice or comment on?

2748   If you could predict one thing and one thing only, what would it be?

2749   What do you do to fight temptation?

2750   What is/was the best thing about being single?

2751   What was the best road trip you've ever had?

2752   What celebrity do you think would make a great world leader?

2753   If you had to live abroad for only one year for work, where would you want to live?

2754   What was the craziest question you ever had to answer on an interview?

2755   How fast do you type?

2756   What fashion faux pas really drive you crazy, like wearing socks with sandals?

2757   What is your greatest insecurity?

2758   If you could predict the future for your life, would you want to know?

2759   If you were like Dorothy traveling the yellow brick road, where would you want it to lead?

2760   What is a game you remember from your childhood?

2761 What is your favorite city beginning with the letter Y?

2762 Have you ever found an unlikely ally, if so who?

2763 Would you ever date someone that had kids from a previous relationship?

2764 What fact do you tell people about yourself that most people think is a lie?

2765 What stereotype do you fit into?

2766 What have you given up on that you wish you never had?

2767 What is your favorite holiday?

2768 Have you ever tie-dyed your own clothes?

2769 What childlike characteristics do you still retain?

2770 Do you like sushi, if so what's your favorite kind?

2771 Would you help a homeless person if they needed mouth-to-mouth resuscitation?

2772 Can you tell when someone is lying to you, if so how?

2773 Do you think people should have to take an IQ test to be able to vote?

2774 If you were a flavor, what flavor would you be?

2775 Are you any good at pool?

2776 What mythological creature or deity fascinates you?

2777 If someone said "today you have to get dirty" what would be the most fun way?

2778 If you were going to become a freelancer, what services would you offer?

2779 Have you started a rumor about anyone and if so who?

2780 When you picture your future, what is one thing that stands out?

2781 What do you do more of when times get hard for you?

2782 What do you do when you've reached a goal you set?

2783 Have you ever studied another form of religion than you were taught, which one?

2784 How paranoid are you?

2785 What instantly melts your heart?

2786 What was your last dream about?

2787 What is the one thing you'd be really disappointed if you never get to experience?

2788 Do you need to slow down in any area of your life?

2789 Would you want to have dual citizenship and what would be the other country?

2790 Has anyone you ever really, really liked thought of you as friend only?

2791 If you could take a class to learn anything, what would it be?

2792 What do you sometimes pretend you understand that you really don't?

2793 How easily do you fall in love, does it take a while or pretty quick?

2794 If you looked at your life right now, is this the life you've dreamed of?

2795 At what point during the last five years have you felt lost?

2796 What excuse do you tell yourself far too often?

2797 What is the biggest problem you've ever solved?

2798 Have you ever done something unbelievable, only to have no one around to see it?

2799 Do you enjoy doing things alone, what specifically?

2800 Do you worry about what people think of you?

2801 In a few words what are your thoughts on gratuity?

2802 What was your favorite age, so far?

2803 How do you feel about the rain?

2804 Who was your first love and where are they now?

2805 What is the last kind thing you did for someone else?

2806   What type of music do you like?

2807   What's the oddest thing you've ever stuck in your ear in place of a Q-tip?

2808   Do you think facial moles or freckles are cute?

2809   Have you ever lied about where you worked, if so what did you say you did?

2810   If you had to describe yourself as cheese, what cheese would you be?

2811   What gives you an eerie feeling?

2812   Have you ever had anything published?

2813   What is your favorite boys' name beginning with the letter D?

2814   Have you ever protested anything?

2815   What conundrum have you ever faced?

2816   If you took up boxing what would be your fighting name?

2817   What is the worst thing that has ever bitten you?

2818   If you could have chosen another profession, what?

2819   Are you a risk taker?

2820   What subject do you and your parents never see eye to eye on?

2821 What are you most compassionate or empathetic about with other people?

2822 How well do you work under pressure?

2823 If you stopped trusting your closest friend would you end the friendship or work on it?

2824 Have you ever had anything stolen, if so what was it?

2825 What types of people make you feel alive?

2826 When playing checkers or chess do you prefer to be black or white?

2827 What is one thing your family wouldn't know about you?

2828 How much do you trust your own instincts?

2829 Who would you want to sing a song you've written?

2830 What mistake do people make that you often correct?

2831 What is your favorite musical instrument beginning with the letter H?

2832 What are you passionate about?

2833 Do you think vanity is a good thing?

2834 When have you lied about your age?

2835 Have you ever had a disastrous interview?

2836   What do you think will be your legacy?

2837   If you had to compare yourself to a historical outlaw, who would it be?

2838   If you could meet your true soulmate but they would die in a year; would you want to?

2839   Have you ever passed out, if so what caused it?

2840   Has someone ever been cold hearted to you, if so how?

2841   Is there anything you are really stingy with?

2842   What scenario was so difficult that you couldn't make a decision so you let someone else?

2843   What is your favorite drink beginning with the letter O?

2844   What things do you wish were avoidable?

2845   Do you believe everything happens for a reason?

2846   Have you ever had a wardrobe malfunction, if so where were you?

2847   Who do you distrust the most in your life?

2848   What makes you moody?

2849   If you became rich would you still continue working?

2850   Do you like spicy food and if so how do you make it spicy?

2851 Where is one place you hope to visit before you die?

2852 Who is the first person you share good news with?

2853 Have you ever sleepwalked?

2854 Every fall the pumpkin spice craze comes, what's your favorite pumpkin spice item?

2855 Do you think there could ever be humans with special powers?

2856 Are putting any part of your life on hold?

2857 Is there something that makes you very sleepy?

2858 On a cold winter's night what warms you up?

2859 If you could go back in history and meet an explorer and join them, who would it be?

2860 Who is your favorite music DJ and what is one thing you like about them?

2861 What is your first thought upon waking up?

2862 What is one thing you wish your resume said?

2863 Do you have a camera that uses conventional film?

2864 What do you love most about a carnival or county fair?

2865 What is the worst thing you deal with about being a man/woman?

2866   Do you have a prediction of when or if the world will ever end?

2867   What does the way you live your life say about you?

2868   Would you join the witness protection program for your own safety if it meant leaving?

2869   What is the worst problem you ever had to solve that you didn't create?

2870   Do you think history is destined to repeat itself?

2871   What historical period would you like to live in if you could go back in time?

2872   In your opinion what makes a bold statement on a person?

2873   What book have you really wanted to read but didn't because it was too long?

2874   Where would you love to travel to but are afraid to go due it being dangerous?

2875   Have you ever been in a play for school or any kind of theatre, if so what was the title?

2876   How important is compatibility in your friendships?

2877   Do you think childhood or adulthood is harder, and in a few words why?

2878   Have you ever broken a promise to yourself?

2879   Are you materialistic?

2880   Are you addicted to selfies?

2881 How do you release your anger?

2882 Are you a selfless person or more selfish?

2883 What was the hardest thing about being a kid for you?

2884 Do you own a gun, would you and why/why not?

2885 What is something people do daily that makes you shake your head in disappointment?

2886 Which do you think is bigger: The World Series or Super Bowl? why?

2887 If you were a farmer, what crop would you want to grow?

2888 If you were serving on a jury, could you sway other jurors if they were divided?

2889 Are you right or left handed and have you tried becoming ambidextrous?

2890 What was the last gift you received that you loved?

2891 Who is your favorite villain/bad guy?

2892 What would be your dream sandwich?

2893 Have you ever been up in a hot-air balloon?

2894 How do you cope with stress?

2895 What lie do you hear over and over?

2896 Which fictional character do you wish was real?

2897 Do you treasure your friendships more than your family?

2898 Have you ever taken the advice "sleep on it" before you make a big decision?

2899 Have you ever wished upon a star?

2900 What 5 world leaders would you make sit down in a room to discuss issues?

2901 Has anyone ever assumed something about you that was untrue, what was it?

2902 Have you served in the military, did you ever consider it and if so what branch?

2903 What sci-fi movie represents how you feel in the mornings?

2904 Do you tend to boss other people or your family members around?

2905 Do you think hard work pays off or is some of it luck?

2906 What is worth fighting for?

2907 Best invention ever made.

2908 Have you ever participated in a reenactment, if so what?

2909 Do you shout out the answers at the TV while watching quiz shows?

2910 Name one thing you did where the risk was well worth the reward?

2911   Have you ever smoked a cigar, would you, for what occasion?

2912   What do you like to pick other people's brains about?

2913   If you could eliminate one disease from the planet forever, what would it be?

2914   Where do you see yourself in 1 year's time?

2915   What empowers you?

2916   What is one thing that makes someone brave in your opinion?

2917   If you were leaving to another planet and could only take 3 things, what would you take?

2918   Have you ever written a love letter?

2919   If you were to give someone "food for thought" what would it be?

2920   What is your favorite smart phone app?

2921   If you could erase someone's memory who would it be and what memory?

2922   Have you ever been left behind somewhere, if so by who and where?

2923   What was the stupidest thing to "trend" in your opinion?

2924   Have you ever played matchmaker with your friends, and did it work out?

2925   Do you like meeting new people?

2926 If you were choosing the next contenders for *Celebrity Death Match* who would it be?

2927 Should schools be allowed to search a student's locker without cause?

2928 Do you think dragons may have been real at some point?

2929 What's your favorite grocery store?

2930 Have you ever taken anything from a hotel, if so what?

2931 Where was the most romantic date you ever had?

2932 Worst experience involving a car?

2933 Do you pray?

2934 What restores your faith?

2935 When you were a kid did your parents let you have a sleepover with friends?

2936 Can you play the harmonica?

2937 If you were going to marry a fictional character who would it be?

2938 What would you do if you had no money?

2939 What or who is your favorite thing to cuddle?

2940 Are you holding a grudge against someone or something, if so what?

2941   Who is your favorite "brand ambassador or mascot"?

2942   What do you try too hard at?

2943   What is your favorite microwavable food?

2944   What is the scariest sound you could hear in the middle of the night?

2945   What is your favorite magazine to read?

2946   What always seems too out of reach for you?

2947   Have you ever been a bad influence on someone?

2948   Do you eat leftovers?

2949   Who do you confide in most often?

2950   Have you ever seen or met your doppelganger?

2951   Do you think the supernatural exists?

2952   Have you ever pitted two people against each other for personal gain, why?

2953   If you were a scratch-n-sniff sticker, what would you be?

2954   Is art really subjective?

2955   Do you have a friend that feels closer to you than family, if so who?

2956 Do you have a favorite coffee mug, if so what's on it or what makes it your favorite?

2957 What cartoon character best describes you?

2958 Have you ever served on a jury? What type of case was it?

2959 Do you value other people's opinion?

2960 Have you ever been horseback riding?

2961 What excites you about the future?

2962 What celebrity would you want as one of your BFFs?

2963 Has anyone ever cheated on you, did you forgive them or could you?

2964 What do you pig out on?

2965 What is your MOST favorite: icecream, gelato, sorbet or frozen yogurt? What flavor?

2966 How do you handle passive aggressive people?

2967 When is communication essential in your opinion?

2968 What female celebrity do you find uniquely beautiful?

2969 Who is the one person you can depend on when you're in trouble?

2970 Regardless of the song, which music video was most creative in your opinion?

2971   When you're alone what memory comes back the most?

2972   Finish this sentence using your sense of humor: It's a bird, it's a plane, no it's...

2973   Do you think children will enhance your life or complicate it?

2974   What makes you feel connected to your family?

2975   Do you like Indian food, if so what's your favorite dish?

2976   If dog's are man's best friend and diamonds are a girl's, then what is your best friend?

2977   What is your favorite job beginning with the letter T?

2978   Who made the best first impression on you?

2979   Who is the most creative person you know?

2980   What is one thing you remember about your childhood home?

2981   What is your pet peeve?

2982   Were you ever a member of any celebrity fan club?

2983   In your opinion what song is the most annoying ever?

2984   Has your life gone according to how you envisioned it?

2985   Were you voted "most likely" for anything in your class yearbook?

2986 Have you ever cheated at a test?

2987 What historic war do you feel was most tragic and which was most beneficial?

2988 What is one interesting fact about your ancestors?

2989 What is your favorite board game?

2990 What's your lucky number?

2991 If you were a member of the Spice Girls, what would your spice handle be?

2992 If technology allowed would you rather live under the ocean or high above the clouds?

2993 What would be your antonym for carpe diem?

2994 What is your favorite Pokémon?

2995 Have you been to the opera or ballet, which was better?

2996 What do you think people undervalue today?

2997 Have you ever bought someone flowers?

2998 Would you ever become a CIA agent, if so why?

2999 What is something you wish you could avoid?

3000 When you're sick do you grin and bear it, or just curl up in bed as much as possible?

Looking for more?

Similar titles available by Piccadilly:

300 Drawing Prompts

500 Drawing Prompts

Complete This Drawing

Sketching Made Easy

Calligraphy Made Easy

Sketch THIS!

Rip it! Write it! Draw it!

300 Writing Prompts

500 Writing Prompts

Complete the Story

Write the Story

Write the Poem

Journal THIS!

The Story of My Life

My Ultimate Bucket List

My Top 10

WWW.PICCADILLYINC.COM